Live N

Journal
365 Days of Interior Freedom

Created by Cameron M. Thompson, Psy.D.

Inspired by the practices of the great witnesses of truth & spiritual freedom of the last century.

Published by

Marchese di Carabàs

Copyright © 2021 Cameron M. Thompson

All rights reserved.

ISBN-13: 978-1-7356578-1-3

AN OPENING MEDITATION

"Only the right name gives beings and things their reality. A wrong name makes everything unreal. That's what lies do."

—Michael Ende, *The Neverending Story*

CONTENTS

INTRODUCTION

This book has one simple purpose: to be a tool for you to free your mind and heart from the system of lies and soft totalitarianism that day by day exerts greater and greater influence in our lives.

This journal is a valuable tool—the like of which preserved the spiritual freedom and sanity of a number of heroic witnesses of truth of the last century even in their darkest hours—in your quest to *live not by lies* and resist the soft totalitarianism that threatens to blot out the truth about reality, human dignity, and our divine calling. Each day you will find herein the opportunity to write about your journey in seeking for, and living in, the truth. This journal will guide you through the opportunity to record the beauty of the truth you see in the world around you, to document the challenges you face each day in living for the sake of truth, and to identify and write down the truth each day so that it cannot be erased or forgotten.

All this can be accomplished in just five minutes a day—time that is sacred, time that is just yours, free from coercion, free from the lies, to simply live in and speak boldly the Truth.

Now we can spend our days blaming the system, blaming "them" and lamenting our alleged helplessness in the situation, or we can stand up—however silently and unnoticed—and root out the lies from within our own hearts first, and so reclaim our lives for the truth. It is easy to blame "them"—there is always an easy "them" to point to—and to throw our hands up in helplessness at our predicament, saying that we can do nothing. But as Solzhenitsyn pointed out long ago, "we can do *everything* (even if we lie to ourselves that this is not so). It is not "they" who are guilty of everything, but *we ourselves*, only *we!*" And we *can* do everything, if only we would take up the necessary tools and commit ourselves to have no longer any part in the lies, but to live whole-heartedly in the truth. This journal aims to be one such tool to help you accomplish and protect this final freedom, the freedom of your own mind, heart, and spirit.

HOW TO USE THIS BOOK

Each day in this journal you will see the following prompts:

1. *"**Gratitude Exercise:** What is one extraordinarily beautiful truth about the world that you noticed today?"*

   — Here I encourage you to reflect on your day in gratitude for the good that is in fact in the world, identify something true and good and beautiful you noticed today. Write it down here.

2. *"**Examine Your Actions:** Where have you been challenged today? Where have you compromised the truth or fail to live up to the fullness of justice? What are your struggles and challenges living for the sake of Truth?"*

   — The greatest obstacle of course is our own complicity with lies and corruption, with compromises against truth, the reality of our own moral frailty. Identifying and owning up to where we fall short allows us to repent, ask forgiveness, and thenceforth grow stronger in living for the truth.

3. *"**Resolution for living in Truth & Freedom:** What concrete thing(s) will you do tomorrow to overcome the lies and live more fully in the truth, no matter the cost?"*

   — Following from your answer to prompt 2, try to name and commit to one specific course of action you can take to overcome these challenges and compromises.

4. *"**A Daily Record of the Truth:** What thoughts, truths, or observations do you want to record today so that they cannot be erased or forgotten?"*

   — This can be open, about anything you wish. This is your speech to speak the truth in freedom.

A PRAYER FOR TRUTH

Grant, O Merciful God, that I may ardently desire, prudently examine, truthfully acknowledge, and perfectly accomplish what is pleasing to you for the praise and glory of your name. Amen.

MEDITATION

"The Course of Truth"

"Him God raised up the third day, and showed Him openly, not to all the people, but unto witnesses chosen before of God."

When royal Truth, released from mortal throes, Burst His brief slumber, and triumphant rose,
  Ill had the Holiest sued
  A patron multitude,
 Or courted Tetrarch's eye, or claim'd to rule
By the world's winning grace, or proofs from learned school.

But, robing Him in viewless air, He told His secret to a few of meanest mould;
  They in their turn imparted
  The gift of men pure-hearted,
 While the brute many heard His mysteries high,
As some strange fearful tongue, and crouch'd, they knew not why.

Still is the might of Truth, as it has been: Lodged in the few, obey'd, and yet unseen.
  Rear'd on lone heights, and rare,
  His saints their watch-flame bear,
 And the mad world sees the wide-circling blaze,
Vain searching whence it streams, and how to quench its rays.

St. John Henry Newman
December 24, 1832.

3

A CALL TO ACTION:
THE LIVE NOT BY LIES MANIFESTO

In the original 1974 underground publication titled "Live Not by Lies," the great anti-totalitarian dissident Alexandre Solzhenitsyn prophetically stated:

> We are approaching the brink; already a universal spiritual demise is upon us; a physical one is about to flare up and engulf us and our children, while we continue to smile sheepishly and babble:
>
> "But what can we do to stop it? We haven't the strength."

Does this not ring all the more true in our day? He goes on to name the very problem that besets us today:

> We have so hopelessly ceded our humanity that for the modest handouts of today we are ready to surrender up all principles, our soul, all the labors of our ancestors, all the prospects of our descendants—anything to avoid disrupting our meager existence. We have lost our strength, our pride, our passion. We do not even fear a common nuclear death, do not fear a third world war (perhaps we'll hide away in some crevice), but fear only to take a civic stance! We hope only not to stray from the herd, not to set out on our own, and risk suddenly having to make do without the comforts of a middle class life...
>
> So has the circle closed? So is there indeed no way out? So the only thing left to do is wait inertly: What if something just happens *by itself?*

But it will never come unstuck *by itself,* if we all, every day, continue to acknowledge, glorify, and strengthen it, if we do not, at the least, recoil from its most vulnerable point.

From lies.

When violence bursts onto the peaceful human condition, its face is flush with self-assurance, it displays on its banner and proclaims: "I am Violence! Make way, step aside, I will crush you!" But violence ages swiftly, a few years pass—and it is no longer sure of itself. To prop itself up, to appear decent, it will without fail call forth its ally—Lies. For violence has nothing to cover itself with but lies, and lies can only persist through violence. And it is not every day and not on every shoulder that violence brings down its heavy hand: It demands of us only a submission to lies, a daily participation in deceit—and this suffices as our fealty.

And therein we find, neglected by us, the simplest, the most accessible key to our liberation: a *personal non-participation in lies!* Even if all is covered by lies, even if all is under their rule, let us resist in the smallest way: Let their rule hold *not through me!*

And this is the way to break out of the imaginary encirclement of our inertness, the easiest way for us and the most devastating for the lies. For when people renounce lies, lies simply cease to exist. Like parasites, they can only survive when attached to a person.

And so what can a person do to break the hold of lies in his or her life? What can you do to quit serving as an accomplice to the lies? Solzhenitsyn offers the following suggestions as starting points, which can serve as a basic promise for each one of us to adhere to.

From this day forth, I commit myself to break the hold of lies in my life and to that end I henceforth...

· WILL NOT WRITE, SIGN, NOR PUBLISH IN ANY WAY, A SINGLE LINE DISTORTING, SO FAR AS I CAN SEE, THE TRUTH;

· WILL NOT UTTER SUCH A LINE IN PRIVATE OR IN PUBLIC CONVERSATION, NOR READ IT FROM A CRIB SHEET, NOR SPEAK IT IN THE ROLE OF EDUCATOR, CANVASSER, TEACHER, ACTOR;

· WILL NOT IN PAINTING, SCULPTURE, PHOTOGRAPH, TECHNOLOGY, OR MUSIC DEPICT, SUPPORT, OR BROADCAST A SINGLE FALSE THOUGHT, A SINGLE DISTORTION OF THE TRUTH AS I DISCERN IT;

· WILL NOT CITE IN WRITING OR IN SPEECH A SINGLE "GUIDING" QUOTE FOR GRATIFICATION, INSURANCE, FOR MY SUCCESS AT WORK, UNLESS I FULLY SHARE THE CITED THOUGHT AND BELIEVE THAT IT FITS THE CONTEXT PRECISELY;

· WILL NOT BE FORCED TO A DEMONSTRATION OR A RALLY IF IT RUNS COUNTER TO MY DESIRE AND MY WILL; WILL NOT TAKE UP AND RAISE A BANNER OR SLOGAN IN WHICH I DO NOT FULLY BELIEVE;

· WILL NOT RAISE A HAND IN VOTE FOR A PROPOSAL WHICH I DO NOT SINCERELY SUPPORT; WILL NOT VOTE OPENLY OR IN SECRET BALLOT FOR A CANDIDATE WHOM I DEEM DUBIOUS OR UNWORTHY;

· WILL NOT BE IMPELLED TO A MEETING WHERE A FORCED AND DISTORTED DISCUSSION IS EXPECTED TO TAKE PLACE;

· WILL AT ONCE WALK OUT FROM A SESSION, MEETING, LECTURE, PLAY, OR FILM AS SOON AS I HEAR THE SPEAKER UTTER A LIE, IDEOLOGICAL DRIVEL, OR SHAMELESS PROPAGANDA;

· WILL NOT SUBSCRIBE TO, NOR BUY IN RETAIL, A NEWSPAPER OR JOURNAL THAT DISTORTS OR HIDES THE UNDERLYING FACTS.

This is by no means an exhaustive list of the possible and necessary ways of evading lies. But those who begin to cleanse themselves from lies will, with a cleansed eye, easily discern yet other opportunities.

Yes, at first it will be unfair. Someone will have to temporarily lose his job. For the young who seek to live by truth, this will at first severely complicate life, for all their tests and quizzes, too, are stuffed with lies, and so choices will have to be made. But there is no loophole left for anyone who seeks to be honest: Not even for a day, not even in the safest technical occupations can he avoid even a single one of the listed choices—to be made in favor of either truth or lies, in favor of spiritual freedom or spiritual servility.

— Alexandre Solzhenitsyn

Now, this is all well and good, but in order to have the strength to hold fast to the truth when push comes to shove (as for many it already has, and for the rest it will come sooner than we wish it), we need to be in the practice of rejecting lies and living in the truth throughout the course of our day-to-day lives. And that is why you have this journal.

So now, with this journal—this precious tool to resist tyranny—in hand and the truth in your mind and heart, resist the darkness and LIVE NOT BY LIES.

THE LIVE NOT BY LIES JOURNAL

365 DAYS OF INTERIOR FREEDOM

Day 1

1. **Gratitude Exercise:** What is one extraordinarily beautiful truth about the world that you noticed today?

_____

_____

_____

2. **Examine Your Actions:** Where have you been challenged today? Where have you compromised the truth or fail to live up to the fullness of justice? What are your struggles and challenges living for the sake of Truth?

_____

_____

_____

3. **Resolution for living in Truth & Freedom:** What concrete thing(s) will you do tomorrow to overcome the lies and live more fully in the truth, no matter the cost?

_____

_____

4. **A Daily Record of the Truth:** What thoughts, truths, or observations do you want to record today so that they cannot be erased or forgotten?

_____

_____

_____

_____

_____

_____

Day 2

1. **Gratitude Exercise:** What is one extraordinarily beautiful truth about the world that you noticed today?

_____

_____

_____

2. **Examine Your Actions:** Where have you been challenged today? Where have you compromised the truth or fail to live up to the fullness of justice? What are your struggles and challenges living for the sake of Truth?

_____

_____

_____

3. **Resolution for living in Truth & Freedom:** What concrete thing(s) will you do tomorrow to overcome the lies and live more fully in the truth, no matter the cost?

_____

_____

4. **A Daily Record of the Truth:** What thoughts, truths, or observations do you want to record today so that they cannot be erased or forgotten?

_____

_____

_____

_____

_____

_____

Day 3

1. **Gratitude Exercise:** What is one extraordinarily beautiful truth about the world that you noticed today?

_____

_____

_____

2. **Examine Your Actions:** Where have you been challenged today? Where have you compromised the truth or fail to live up to the fullness of justice? What are your struggles and challenges living for the sake of Truth?

_____

_____

_____

3. **Resolution for living in Truth & Freedom:** What concrete thing(s) will you do tomorrow to overcome the lies and live more fully in the truth, no matter the cost?

_____

_____

4. **A Daily Record of the Truth:** What thoughts, truths, or observations do you want to record today so that they cannot be erased or forgotten?

_____

_____

_____

_____

_____

_____

Day 4

1. **Gratitude Exercise:** What is one extraordinarily beautiful truth about the world that you noticed today?

\
\
\

2. **Examine Your Actions:** Where have you been challenged today? Where have you compromised the truth or fail to live up to the fullness of justice? What are your struggles and challenges living for the sake of Truth?

\
\
\

3. **Resolution for living in Truth & Freedom:** What concrete thing(s) will you do tomorrow to overcome the lies and live more fully in the truth, no matter the cost?

\
\

4. **A Daily Record of the Truth:** What thoughts, truths, or observations do you want to record today so that they cannot be erased or forgotten?

\
\
\
\
\
\

Day 5

1. **Gratitude Exercise:** What is one extraordinarily beautiful truth about the world that you noticed today?

_____

_____

_____

2. **Examine Your Actions:** Where have you been challenged today? Where have you compromised the truth or fail to live up to the fullness of justice? What are your struggles and challenges living for the sake of Truth?

_____

_____

_____

3. **Resolution for living in Truth & Freedom:** What concrete thing(s) will you do tomorrow to overcome the lies and live more fully in the truth, no matter the cost?

_____

_____

4. **A Daily Record of the Truth:** What thoughts, truths, or observations do you want to record today so that they cannot be erased or forgotten?

_____

_____

_____

_____

_____

_____

Day 6

1. **Gratitude Exercise:** What is one extraordinarily beautiful truth about the world that you noticed today?

    _____

    _____

    _____

2. **Examine Your Actions:** Where have you been challenged today? Where have you compromised the truth or fail to live up to the fullness of justice? What are your struggles and challenges living for the sake of Truth?

    _____

    _____

    _____

3. **Resolution for living in Truth & Freedom:** What concrete thing(s) will you do tomorrow to overcome the lies and live more fully in the truth, no matter the cost?

    _____

    _____

4. **A Daily Record of the Truth:** What thoughts, truths, or observations do you want to record today so that they cannot be erased or forgotten?

    _____

    _____

    _____

    _____

    _____

    _____

Day 7

1. **Gratitude Exercise:** What is one extraordinarily beautiful truth about the world that you noticed today?

_____

_____

_____

2. **Examine Your Actions:** Where have you been challenged today? Where have you compromised the truth or fail to live up to the fullness of justice? What are your struggles and challenges living for the sake of Truth?

_____

_____

_____

3. **Resolution for living in Truth & Freedom:** What concrete thing(s) will you do tomorrow to overcome the lies and live more fully in the truth, no matter the cost?

_____

_____

4. **A Daily Record of the Truth:** What thoughts, truths, or observations do you want to record today so that they cannot be erased or forgotten?

_____

_____

_____

_____

_____

_____

Day 8

1. **Gratitude Exercise:** What is one extraordinarily beautiful truth about the world that you noticed today?

_____

_____

_____

2. **Examine Your Actions:** Where have you been challenged today? Where have you compromised the truth or fail to live up to the fullness of justice? What are your struggles and challenges living for the sake of Truth?

_____

_____

_____

3. **Resolution for living in Truth & Freedom:** What concrete thing(s) will you do tomorrow to overcome the lies and live more fully in the truth, no matter the cost?

_____

_____

4. **A Daily Record of the Truth:** What thoughts, truths, or observations do you want to record today so that they cannot be erased or forgotten?

_____

_____

_____

_____

_____

_____

Day 9

1. **Gratitude Exercise:** What is one extraordinarily beautiful truth about the world that you noticed today?

_____

_____

_____

2. **Examine Your Actions:** Where have you been challenged today? Where have you compromised the truth or fail to live up to the fullness of justice? What are your struggles and challenges living for the sake of Truth?

_____

_____

_____

3. **Resolution for living in Truth & Freedom:** What concrete thing(s) will you do tomorrow to overcome the lies and live more fully in the truth, no matter the cost?

_____

_____

4. **A Daily Record of the Truth:** What thoughts, truths, or observations do you want to record today so that they cannot be erased or forgotten?

_____

_____

_____

_____

_____

Day 10

1. **Gratitude Exercise:** What is one extraordinarily beautiful truth about the world that you noticed today?

_____

_____

_____

2. **Examine Your Actions:** Where have you been challenged today? Where have you compromised the truth or fail to live up to the fullness of justice? What are your struggles and challenges living for the sake of Truth?

_____

_____

_____

3. **Resolution for living in Truth & Freedom:** What concrete thing(s) will you do tomorrow to overcome the lies and live more fully in the truth, no matter the cost?

_____

_____

4. **A Daily Record of the Truth:** What thoughts, truths, or observations do you want to record today so that they cannot be erased or forgotten?

_____

_____

_____

_____

_____

_____

Day 11

1. **Gratitude Exercise:** What is one extraordinarily beautiful truth about the world that you noticed today?

_____

_____

_____

2. **Examine Your Actions:** Where have you been challenged today? Where have you compromised the truth or fail to live up to the fullness of justice? What are your struggles and challenges living for the sake of Truth?

_____

_____

_____

3. **Resolution for living in Truth & Freedom:** What concrete thing(s) will you do tomorrow to overcome the lies and live more fully in the truth, no matter the cost?

_____

_____

4. **A Daily Record of the Truth:** What thoughts, truths, or observations do you want to record today so that they cannot be erased or forgotten?

_____

_____

_____

_____

_____

_____

Day 12

1. **Gratitude Exercise:** What is one extraordinarily beautiful truth about the world that you noticed today?

   _____

   _____

   _____

2. **Examine Your Actions:** Where have you been challenged today? Where have you compromised the truth or fail to live up to the fullness of justice? What are your struggles and challenges living for the sake of Truth?

   _____

   _____

   _____

3. **Resolution for living in Truth & Freedom:** What concrete thing(s) will you do tomorrow to overcome the lies and live more fully in the truth, no matter the cost?

   _____

   _____

4. **A Daily Record of the Truth:** What thoughts, truths, or observations do you want to record today so that they cannot be erased or forgotten?

   _____

   _____

   _____

   _____

   _____

   _____

Day 13

1. **Gratitude Exercise:** What is one extraordinarily beautiful truth about the world that you noticed today?

_____

_____

_____

2. **Examine Your Actions:** Where have you been challenged today? Where have you compromised the truth or fail to live up to the fullness of justice? What are your struggles and challenges living for the sake of Truth?

_____

_____

_____

3. **Resolution for living in Truth & Freedom:** What concrete thing(s) will you do tomorrow to overcome the lies and live more fully in the truth, no matter the cost?

_____

_____

4. **A Daily Record of the Truth:** What thoughts, truths, or observations do you want to record today so that they cannot be erased or forgotten?

_____

_____

_____

_____

_____

Day 14

1. **Gratitude Exercise:** What is one extraordinarily beautiful truth about the world that you noticed today?

   _____

   _____

   _____

2. **Examine Your Actions:** Where have you been challenged today? Where have you compromised the truth or fail to live up to the fullness of justice? What are your struggles and challenges living for the sake of Truth?

   _____

   _____

   _____

3. **Resolution for living in Truth & Freedom:** What concrete thing(s) will you do tomorrow to overcome the lies and live more fully in the truth, no matter the cost?

   _____

   _____

4. **A Daily Record of the Truth:** What thoughts, truths, or observations do you want to record today so that they cannot be erased or forgotten?

   _____

   _____

   _____

   _____

   _____

   _____

Day 15

1. **Gratitude Exercise:** What is one extraordinarily beautiful truth about the world that you noticed today?

   _____

   _____

   _____

2. **Examine Your Actions:** Where have you been challenged today? Where have you compromised the truth or fail to live up to the fullness of justice? What are your struggles and challenges living for the sake of Truth?

   _____

   _____

   _____

3. **Resolution for living in Truth & Freedom:** What concrete thing(s) will you do tomorrow to overcome the lies and live more fully in the truth, no matter the cost?

   _____

   _____

4. **A Daily Record of the Truth:** What thoughts, truths, or observations do you want to record today so that they cannot be erased or forgotten?

   _____

   _____

   _____

   _____

   _____

   _____

Day 16

1. **Gratitude Exercise:** What is one extraordinarily beautiful truth about the world that you noticed today?

_____

_____

_____

2. **Examine Your Actions:** Where have you been challenged today? Where have you compromised the truth or fail to live up to the fullness of justice? What are your struggles and challenges living for the sake of Truth?

_____

_____

_____

3. **Resolution for living in Truth & Freedom:** What concrete thing(s) will you do tomorrow to overcome the lies and live more fully in the truth, no matter the cost?

_____

_____

4. **A Daily Record of the Truth:** What thoughts, truths, or observations do you want to record today so that they cannot be erased or forgotten?

_____

_____

_____

_____

_____

_____

Day 17

1. **Gratitude Exercise:** What is one extraordinarily beautiful truth about the world that you noticed today?

_____

_____

_____

2. **Examine Your Actions:** Where have you been challenged today? Where have you compromised the truth or fail to live up to the fullness of justice? What are your struggles and challenges living for the sake of Truth?

_____

_____

_____

3. **Resolution for living in Truth & Freedom:** What concrete thing(s) will you do tomorrow to overcome the lies and live more fully in the truth, no matter the cost?

_____

_____

4. **A Daily Record of the Truth:** What thoughts, truths, or observations do you want to record today so that they cannot be erased or forgotten?

_____

_____

_____

_____

_____

_____

Day 18

1. **Gratitude Exercise:** What is one extraordinarily beautiful truth about the world that you noticed today?

_____

_____

_____

2. **Examine Your Actions:** Where have you been challenged today? Where have you compromised the truth or fail to live up to the fullness of justice? What are your struggles and challenges living for the sake of Truth?

_____

_____

_____

3. **Resolution for living in Truth & Freedom:** What concrete thing(s) will you do tomorrow to overcome the lies and live more fully in the truth, no matter the cost?

_____

_____

4. **A Daily Record of the Truth:** What thoughts, truths, or observations do you want to record today so that they cannot be erased or forgotten?

_____

_____

_____

_____

_____

_____

Day 19

1. **Gratitude Exercise:** What is one extraordinarily beautiful truth about the world that you noticed today?

_____

_____

_____

2. **Examine Your Actions:** Where have you been challenged today? Where have you compromised the truth or fail to live up to the fullness of justice? What are your struggles and challenges living for the sake of Truth?

_____

_____

_____

3. **Resolution for living in Truth & Freedom:** What concrete thing(s) will you do tomorrow to overcome the lies and live more fully in the truth, no matter the cost?

_____

_____

4. **A Daily Record of the Truth:** What thoughts, truths, or observations do you want to record today so that they cannot be erased or forgotten?

_____

_____

_____

_____

_____

_____

Day 20

1. **Gratitude Exercise:** What is one extraordinarily beautiful truth about the world that you noticed today?

_____

_____

_____

2. **Examine Your Actions:** Where have you been challenged today? Where have you compromised the truth or fail to live up to the fullness of justice? What are your struggles and challenges living for the sake of Truth?

_____

_____

_____

3. **Resolution for living in Truth & Freedom:** What concrete thing(s) will you do tomorrow to overcome the lies and live more fully in the truth, no matter the cost?

_____

_____

4. **A Daily Record of the Truth:** What thoughts, truths, or observations do you want to record today so that they cannot be erased or forgotten?

_____

_____

_____

_____

_____

_____

Day 21

1. **Gratitude Exercise:** What is one extraordinarily beautiful truth about the world that you noticed today?

_____

_____

_____

2. **Examine Your Actions:** Where have you been challenged today? Where have you compromised the truth or fail to live up to the fullness of justice? What are your struggles and challenges living for the sake of Truth?

_____

_____

_____

3. **Resolution for living in Truth & Freedom:** What concrete thing(s) will you do tomorrow to overcome the lies and live more fully in the truth, no matter the cost?

_____

_____

4. **A Daily Record of the Truth:** What thoughts, truths, or observations do you want to record today so that they cannot be erased or forgotten?

_____

_____

_____

_____

_____

_____

Day 22

1. **Gratitude Exercise:** What is one extraordinarily beautiful truth about the world that you noticed today?

_____

_____

_____

2. **Examine Your Actions:** Where have you been challenged today? Where have you compromised the truth or fail to live up to the fullness of justice? What are your struggles and challenges living for the sake of Truth?

_____

_____

_____

3. **Resolution for living in Truth & Freedom:** What concrete thing(s) will you do tomorrow to overcome the lies and live more fully in the truth, no matter the cost?

_____

_____

4. **A Daily Record of the Truth:** What thoughts, truths, or observations do you want to record today so that they cannot be erased or forgotten?

_____

_____

_____

_____

_____

Day 23

1. **Gratitude Exercise:** What is one extraordinarily beautiful truth about the world that you noticed today?

_____

_____

_____

2. **Examine Your Actions:** Where have you been challenged today? Where have you compromised the truth or fail to live up to the fullness of justice? What are your struggles and challenges living for the sake of Truth?

_____

_____

_____

3. **Resolution for living in Truth & Freedom:** What concrete thing(s) will you do tomorrow to overcome the lies and live more fully in the truth, no matter the cost?

_____

_____

4. **A Daily Record of the Truth:** What thoughts, truths, or observations do you want to record today so that they cannot be erased or forgotten?

_____

_____

_____

_____

_____

_____

Day 24

1. **Gratitude Exercise:** What is one extraordinarily beautiful truth about the world that you noticed today?

_____

_____

_____

2. **Examine Your Actions:** Where have you been challenged today? Where have you compromised the truth or fail to live up to the fullness of justice? What are your struggles and challenges living for the sake of Truth?

_____

_____

_____

3. **Resolution for living in Truth & Freedom:** What concrete thing(s) will you do tomorrow to overcome the lies and live more fully in the truth, no matter the cost?

_____

_____

4. **A Daily Record of the Truth:** What thoughts, truths, or observations do you want to record today so that they cannot be erased or forgotten?

_____

_____

_____

_____

_____

_____

Day 25

1. **Gratitude Exercise:** What is one extraordinarily beautiful truth about the world that you noticed today?

_____

_____

_____

2. **Examine Your Actions:** Where have you been challenged today? Where have you compromised the truth or fail to live up to the fullness of justice? What are your struggles and challenges living for the sake of Truth?

_____

_____

_____

3. **Resolution for living in Truth & Freedom:** What concrete thing(s) will you do tomorrow to overcome the lies and live more fully in the truth, no matter the cost?

_____

_____

4. **A Daily Record of the Truth:** What thoughts, truths, or observations do you want to record today so that they cannot be erased or forgotten?

_____

_____

_____

_____

_____

_____

Day 26

1. **Gratitude Exercise:** What is one extraordinarily beautiful truth about the world that you noticed today?

    _____

    _____

    _____

2. **Examine Your Actions:** Where have you been challenged today? Where have you compromised the truth or fail to live up to the fullness of justice? What are your struggles and challenges living for the sake of Truth?

    _____

    _____

    _____

3. **Resolution for living in Truth & Freedom:** What concrete thing(s) will you do tomorrow to overcome the lies and live more fully in the truth, no matter the cost?

    _____

    _____

4. **A Daily Record of the Truth:** What thoughts, truths, or observations do you want to record today so that they cannot be erased or forgotten?

    _____

    _____

    _____

    _____

    _____

    _____

Day 27

1. **Gratitude Exercise:** What is one extraordinarily beautiful truth about the world that you noticed today?

_____

_____

_____

2. **Examine Your Actions:** Where have you been challenged today? Where have you compromised the truth or fail to live up to the fullness of justice? What are your struggles and challenges living for the sake of Truth?

_____

_____

_____

3. **Resolution for living in Truth & Freedom:** What concrete thing(s) will you do tomorrow to overcome the lies and live more fully in the truth, no matter the cost?

_____

_____

4. **A Daily Record of the Truth:** What thoughts, truths, or observations do you want to record today so that they cannot be erased or forgotten?

_____

_____

_____

_____

_____

_____

Day 28

1. **Gratitude Exercise:** What is one extraordinarily beautiful truth about the world that you noticed today?

_____

_____

_____

2. **Examine Your Actions:** Where have you been challenged today? Where have you compromised the truth or fail to live up to the fullness of justice? What are your struggles and challenges living for the sake of Truth?

_____

_____

_____

3. **Resolution for living in Truth & Freedom:** What concrete thing(s) will you do tomorrow to overcome the lies and live more fully in the truth, no matter the cost?

_____

_____

4. **A Daily Record of the Truth:** What thoughts, truths, or observations do you want to record today so that they cannot be erased or forgotten?

_____

_____

_____

_____

_____

_____

Day 29

1. **Gratitude Exercise:** What is one extraordinarily beautiful truth about the world that you noticed today?

_____

_____

_____

2. **Examine Your Actions:** Where have you been challenged today? Where have you compromised the truth or fail to live up to the fullness of justice? What are your struggles and challenges living for the sake of Truth?

_____

_____

_____

3. **Resolution for living in Truth & Freedom:** What concrete thing(s) will you do tomorrow to overcome the lies and live more fully in the truth, no matter the cost?

_____

_____

4. **A Daily Record of the Truth:** What thoughts, truths, or observations do you want to record today so that they cannot be erased or forgotten?

_____

_____

_____

_____

_____

_____

Day 30

1. **Gratitude Exercise:** What is one extraordinarily beautiful truth about the world that you noticed today?

   _____

   _____

   _____

2. **Examine Your Actions:** Where have you been challenged today? Where have you compromised the truth or fail to live up to the fullness of justice? What are your struggles and challenges living for the sake of Truth?

   _____

   _____

   _____

3. **Resolution for living in Truth & Freedom:** What concrete thing(s) will you do tomorrow to overcome the lies and live more fully in the truth, no matter the cost?

   _____

   _____

4. **A Daily Record of the Truth:** What thoughts, truths, or observations do you want to record today so that they cannot be erased or forgotten?

   _____

   _____

   _____

   _____

   _____

   _____

Day 31

1. **Gratitude Exercise:** What is one extraordinarily beautiful truth about the world that you noticed today?

_____

_____

_____

2. **Examine Your Actions:** Where have you been challenged today? Where have you compromised the truth or fail to live up to the fullness of justice? What are your struggles and challenges living for the sake of Truth?

_____

_____

_____

3. **Resolution for living in Truth & Freedom:** What concrete thing(s) will you do tomorrow to overcome the lies and live more fully in the truth, no matter the cost?

_____

_____

4. **A Daily Record of the Truth:** What thoughts, truths, or observations do you want to record today so that they cannot be erased or forgotten?

_____

_____

_____

_____

_____

Day 32

1. **Gratitude Exercise:** What is one extraordinarily beautiful truth about the world that you noticed today?

_____

_____

_____

2. **Examine Your Actions:** Where have you been challenged today? Where have you compromised the truth or fail to live up to the fullness of justice? What are your struggles and challenges living for the sake of Truth?

_____

_____

_____

3. **Resolution for living in Truth & Freedom:** What concrete thing(s) will you do tomorrow to overcome the lies and live more fully in the truth, no matter the cost?

_____

_____

4. **A Daily Record of the Truth:** What thoughts, truths, or observations do you want to record today so that they cannot be erased or forgotten?

_____

_____

_____

_____

_____

_____

Day 33

1. **Gratitude Exercise:** What is one extraordinarily beautiful truth about the world that you noticed today?

_____

_____

_____

2. **Examine Your Actions:** Where have you been challenged today? Where have you compromised the truth or fail to live up to the fullness of justice? What are your struggles and challenges living for the sake of Truth?

_____

_____

_____

3. **Resolution for living in Truth & Freedom:** What concrete thing(s) will you do tomorrow to overcome the lies and live more fully in the truth, no matter the cost?

_____

_____

4. **A Daily Record of the Truth:** What thoughts, truths, or observations do you want to record today so that they cannot be erased or forgotten?

_____

_____

_____

_____

_____

_____

Day 34

1. **Gratitude Exercise:** What is one extraordinarily beautiful truth about the world that you noticed today?

_____

_____

_____

2. **Examine Your Actions:** Where have you been challenged today? Where have you compromised the truth or fail to live up to the fullness of justice? What are your struggles and challenges living for the sake of Truth?

_____

_____

_____

3. **Resolution for living in Truth & Freedom:** What concrete thing(s) will you do tomorrow to overcome the lies and live more fully in the truth, no matter the cost?

_____

_____

4. **A Daily Record of the Truth:** What thoughts, truths, or observations do you want to record today so that they cannot be erased or forgotten?

_____

_____

_____

_____

_____

_____

Day 35

1. **Gratitude Exercise:** What is one extraordinarily beautiful truth about the world that you noticed today?

   _____

   _____

   _____

2. **Examine Your Actions:** Where have you been challenged today? Where have you compromised the truth or fail to live up to the fullness of justice? What are your struggles and challenges living for the sake of Truth?

   _____

   _____

   _____

3. **Resolution for living in Truth & Freedom:** What concrete thing(s) will you do tomorrow to overcome the lies and live more fully in the truth, no matter the cost?

   _____

   _____

4. **A Daily Record of the Truth:** What thoughts, truths, or observations do you want to record today so that they cannot be erased or forgotten?

   _____

   _____

   _____

   _____

   _____

   _____

Day 36

1. **Gratitude Exercise:** What is one extraordinarily beautiful truth about the world that you noticed today?

_____

_____

_____

2. **Examine Your Actions:** Where have you been challenged today? Where have you compromised the truth or fail to live up to the fullness of justice? What are your struggles and challenges living for the sake of Truth?

_____

_____

_____

3. **Resolution for living in Truth & Freedom:** What concrete thing(s) will you do tomorrow to overcome the lies and live more fully in the truth, no matter the cost?

_____

_____

4. **A Daily Record of the Truth:** What thoughts, truths, or observations do you want to record today so that they cannot be erased or forgotten?

_____

_____

_____

_____

_____

_____

Day 37

1. **Gratitude Exercise:** What is one extraordinarily beautiful truth about the world that you noticed today?

_____

_____

_____

2. **Examine Your Actions:** Where have you been challenged today? Where have you compromised the truth or fail to live up to the fullness of justice? What are your struggles and challenges living for the sake of Truth?

_____

_____

_____

3. **Resolution for living in Truth & Freedom:** What concrete thing(s) will you do tomorrow to overcome the lies and live more fully in the truth, no matter the cost?

_____

_____

4. **A Daily Record of the Truth:** What thoughts, truths, or observations do you want to record today so that they cannot be erased or forgotten?

_____

_____

_____

_____

_____

_____

Day 38

1. **Gratitude Exercise:** What is one extraordinarily beautiful truth about the world that you noticed today?

_____

_____

_____

2. **Examine Your Actions:** Where have you been challenged today? Where have you compromised the truth or fail to live up to the fullness of justice? What are your struggles and challenges living for the sake of Truth?

_____

_____

_____

3. **Resolution for living in Truth & Freedom:** What concrete thing(s) will you do tomorrow to overcome the lies and live more fully in the truth, no matter the cost?

_____

_____

4. **A Daily Record of the Truth:** What thoughts, truths, or observations do you want to record today so that they cannot be erased or forgotten?

_____

_____

_____

_____

_____

_____

Day 39

1. **Gratitude Exercise:** What is one extraordinarily beautiful truth about the world that you noticed today?

_____

_____

_____

2. **Examine Your Actions:** Where have you been challenged today? Where have you compromised the truth or fail to live up to the fullness of justice? What are your struggles and challenges living for the sake of Truth?

_____

_____

_____

3. **Resolution for living in Truth & Freedom:** What concrete thing(s) will you do tomorrow to overcome the lies and live more fully in the truth, no matter the cost?

_____

_____

4. **A Daily Record of the Truth:** What thoughts, truths, or observations do you want to record today so that they cannot be erased or forgotten?

_____

_____

_____

_____

_____

_____

Day 40

1. **Gratitude Exercise:** What is one extraordinarily beautiful truth about the world that you noticed today?

_____

_____

_____

2. **Examine Your Actions:** Where have you been challenged today? Where have you compromised the truth or fail to live up to the fullness of justice? What are your struggles and challenges living for the sake of Truth?

_____

_____

_____

3. **Resolution for living in Truth & Freedom:** What concrete thing(s) will you do tomorrow to overcome the lies and live more fully in the truth, no matter the cost?

_____

_____

4. **A Daily Record of the Truth:** What thoughts, truths, or observations do you want to record today so that they cannot be erased or forgotten?

_____

_____

_____

_____

_____

_____

Day 41

1. **Gratitude Exercise:** What is one extraordinarily beautiful truth about the world that you noticed today?

_____

_____

_____

2. **Examine Your Actions:** Where have you been challenged today? Where have you compromised the truth or fail to live up to the fullness of justice? What are your struggles and challenges living for the sake of Truth?

_____

_____

_____

3. **Resolution for living in Truth & Freedom:** What concrete thing(s) will you do tomorrow to overcome the lies and live more fully in the truth, no matter the cost?

_____

_____

4. **A Daily Record of the Truth:** What thoughts, truths, or observations do you want to record today so that they cannot be erased or forgotten?

_____

_____

_____

_____

_____

_____

Day 42

1. **Gratitude Exercise:** What is one extraordinarily beautiful truth about the world that you noticed today?

_____

_____

_____

2. **Examine Your Actions:** Where have you been challenged today? Where have you compromised the truth or fail to live up to the fullness of justice? What are your struggles and challenges living for the sake of Truth?

_____

_____

_____

3. **Resolution for living in Truth & Freedom:** What concrete thing(s) will you do tomorrow to overcome the lies and live more fully in the truth, no matter the cost?

_____

_____

4. **A Daily Record of the Truth:** What thoughts, truths, or observations do you want to record today so that they cannot be erased or forgotten?

_____

_____

_____

_____

_____

_____

Day 43

1. **Gratitude Exercise:** What is one extraordinarily beautiful truth about the world that you noticed today?

_____

_____

_____

2. **Examine Your Actions:** Where have you been challenged today? Where have you compromised the truth or fail to live up to the fullness of justice? What are your struggles and challenges living for the sake of Truth?

_____

_____

_____

3. **Resolution for living in Truth & Freedom:** What concrete thing(s) will you do tomorrow to overcome the lies and live more fully in the truth, no matter the cost?

_____

_____

4. **A Daily Record of the Truth:** What thoughts, truths, or observations do you want to record today so that they cannot be erased or forgotten?

_____

_____

_____

_____

_____

_____

Day 44

1. **Gratitude Exercise:** What is one extraordinarily beautiful truth about the world that you noticed today?

_____

_____

_____

2. **Examine Your Actions:** Where have you been challenged today? Where have you compromised the truth or fail to live up to the fullness of justice? What are your struggles and challenges living for the sake of Truth?

_____

_____

_____

3. **Resolution for living in Truth & Freedom:** What concrete thing(s) will you do tomorrow to overcome the lies and live more fully in the truth, no matter the cost?

_____

_____

4. **A Daily Record of the Truth:** What thoughts, truths, or observations do you want to record today so that they cannot be erased or forgotten?

_____

_____

_____

_____

_____

_____

Day 45

1. **Gratitude Exercise:** What is one extraordinarily beautiful truth about the world that you noticed today?

_____

_____

_____

2. **Examine Your Actions:** Where have you been challenged today? Where have you compromised the truth or fail to live up to the fullness of justice? What are your struggles and challenges living for the sake of Truth?

_____

_____

_____

3. **Resolution for living in Truth & Freedom:** What concrete thing(s) will you do tomorrow to overcome the lies and live more fully in the truth, no matter the cost?

_____

_____

4. **A Daily Record of the Truth:** What thoughts, truths, or observations do you want to record today so that they cannot be erased or forgotten?

_____

_____

_____

_____

_____

Day 46

1. **Gratitude Exercise:** What is one extraordinarily beautiful truth about the world that you noticed today?

_____

_____

_____

2. **Examine Your Actions:** Where have you been challenged today? Where have you compromised the truth or fail to live up to the fullness of justice? What are your struggles and challenges living for the sake of Truth?

_____

_____

_____

3. **Resolution for living in Truth & Freedom:** What concrete thing(s) will you do tomorrow to overcome the lies and live more fully in the truth, no matter the cost?

_____

_____

4. **A Daily Record of the Truth:** What thoughts, truths, or observations do you want to record today so that they cannot be erased or forgotten?

_____

_____

_____

_____

_____

Day 47

1. **Gratitude Exercise:** What is one extraordinarily beautiful truth about the world that you noticed today?

_____

_____

_____

2. **Examine Your Actions:** Where have you been challenged today? Where have you compromised the truth or fail to live up to the fullness of justice? What are your struggles and challenges living for the sake of Truth?

_____

_____

_____

3. **Resolution for living in Truth & Freedom:** What concrete thing(s) will you do tomorrow to overcome the lies and live more fully in the truth, no matter the cost?

_____

_____

4. **A Daily Record of the Truth:** What thoughts, truths, or observations do you want to record today so that they cannot be erased or forgotten?

_____

_____

_____

_____

_____

_____

Day 48

1. **Gratitude Exercise:** What is one extraordinarily beautiful truth about the world that you noticed today?

_____

_____

_____

2. **Examine Your Actions:** Where have you been challenged today? Where have you compromised the truth or fail to live up to the fullness of justice? What are your struggles and challenges living for the sake of Truth?

_____

_____

_____

3. **Resolution for living in Truth & Freedom:** What concrete thing(s) will you do tomorrow to overcome the lies and live more fully in the truth, no matter the cost?

_____

_____

4. **A Daily Record of the Truth:** What thoughts, truths, or observations do you want to record today so that they cannot be erased or forgotten?

_____

_____

_____

_____

_____

_____

Day 49

1. **Gratitude Exercise:** What is one extraordinarily beautiful truth about the world that you noticed today?

   _____

   _____

   _____

2. **Examine Your Actions:** Where have you been challenged today? Where have you compromised the truth or fail to live up to the fullness of justice? What are your struggles and challenges living for the sake of Truth?

   _____

   _____

   _____

3. **Resolution for living in Truth & Freedom:** What concrete thing(s) will you do tomorrow to overcome the lies and live more fully in the truth, no matter the cost?

   _____

   _____

4. **A Daily Record of the Truth:** What thoughts, truths, or observations do you want to record today so that they cannot be erased or forgotten?

   _____

   _____

   _____

   _____

   _____

   _____

Day 50

1. **Gratitude Exercise:** What is one extraordinarily beautiful truth about the world that you noticed today?

_____

_____

_____

2. **Examine Your Actions:** Where have you been challenged today? Where have you compromised the truth or fail to live up to the fullness of justice? What are your struggles and challenges living for the sake of Truth?

_____

_____

_____

3. **Resolution for living in Truth & Freedom:** What concrete thing(s) will you do tomorrow to overcome the lies and live more fully in the truth, no matter the cost?

_____

_____

4. **A Daily Record of the Truth:** What thoughts, truths, or observations do you want to record today so that they cannot be erased or forgotten?

_____

_____

_____

_____

_____

_____

Day 51

1. **Gratitude Exercise:** What is one extraordinarily beautiful truth about the world that you noticed today?

_____

_____

_____

2. **Examine Your Actions:** Where have you been challenged today? Where have you compromised the truth or fail to live up to the fullness of justice? What are your struggles and challenges living for the sake of Truth?

_____

_____

_____

3. **Resolution for living in Truth & Freedom:** What concrete thing(s) will you do tomorrow to overcome the lies and live more fully in the truth, no matter the cost?

_____

_____

4. **A Daily Record of the Truth:** What thoughts, truths, or observations do you want to record today so that they cannot be erased or forgotten?

_____

_____

_____

_____

_____

_____

Day 52

1. **Gratitude Exercise:** What is one extraordinarily beautiful truth about the world that you noticed today?

   _____

   _____

   _____

2. **Examine Your Actions:** Where have you been challenged today? Where have you compromised the truth or fail to live up to the fullness of justice? What are your struggles and challenges living for the sake of Truth?

   _____

   _____

   _____

3. **Resolution for living in Truth & Freedom:** What concrete thing(s) will you do tomorrow to overcome the lies and live more fully in the truth, no matter the cost?

   _____

   _____

4. **A Daily Record of the Truth:** What thoughts, truths, or observations do you want to record today so that they cannot be erased or forgotten?

   _____

   _____

   _____

   _____

   _____

   _____

Day 53

1. **Gratitude Exercise:** What is one extraordinarily beautiful truth about the world that you noticed today?

_____

_____

_____

2. **Examine Your Actions:** Where have you been challenged today? Where have you compromised the truth or fail to live up to the fullness of justice? What are your struggles and challenges living for the sake of Truth?

_____

_____

_____

3. **Resolution for living in Truth & Freedom:** What concrete thing(s) will you do tomorrow to overcome the lies and live more fully in the truth, no matter the cost?

_____

_____

4. **A Daily Record of the Truth:** What thoughts, truths, or observations do you want to record today so that they cannot be erased or forgotten?

_____

_____

_____

_____

_____

_____

Day 54

1. **Gratitude Exercise:** What is one extraordinarily beautiful truth about the world that you noticed today?

_____

_____

_____

2. **Examine Your Actions:** Where have you been challenged today? Where have you compromised the truth or fail to live up to the fullness of justice? What are your struggles and challenges living for the sake of Truth?

_____

_____

_____

3. **Resolution for living in Truth & Freedom:** What concrete thing(s) will you do tomorrow to overcome the lies and live more fully in the truth, no matter the cost?

_____

_____

4. **A Daily Record of the Truth:** What thoughts, truths, or observations do you want to record today so that they cannot be erased or forgotten?

_____

_____

_____

_____

_____

_____

Day 55

1. **Gratitude Exercise:** What is one extraordinarily beautiful truth about the world that you noticed today?

_____

_____

_____

2. **Examine Your Actions:** Where have you been challenged today? Where have you compromised the truth or fail to live up to the fullness of justice? What are your struggles and challenges living for the sake of Truth?

_____

_____

_____

3. **Resolution for living in Truth & Freedom:** What concrete thing(s) will you do tomorrow to overcome the lies and live more fully in the truth, no matter the cost?

_____

_____

4. **A Daily Record of the Truth:** What thoughts, truths, or observations do you want to record today so that they cannot be erased or forgotten?

_____

_____

_____

_____

_____

_____

Day 56

1. **Gratitude Exercise:** What is one extraordinarily beautiful truth about the world that you noticed today?

_____

_____

_____

2. **Examine Your Actions:** Where have you been challenged today? Where have you compromised the truth or fail to live up to the fullness of justice? What are your struggles and challenges living for the sake of Truth?

_____

_____

_____

3. **Resolution for living in Truth & Freedom:** What concrete thing(s) will you do tomorrow to overcome the lies and live more fully in the truth, no matter the cost?

_____

_____

4. **A Daily Record of the Truth:** What thoughts, truths, or observations do you want to record today so that they cannot be erased or forgotten?

_____

_____

_____

_____

_____

_____

Day 57

1. **Gratitude Exercise:** What is one extraordinarily beautiful truth about the world that you noticed today?

_____

_____

_____

2. **Examine Your Actions:** Where have you been challenged today? Where have you compromised the truth or fail to live up to the fullness of justice? What are your struggles and challenges living for the sake of Truth?

_____

_____

_____

3. **Resolution for living in Truth & Freedom:** What concrete thing(s) will you do tomorrow to overcome the lies and live more fully in the truth, no matter the cost?

_____

_____

4. **A Daily Record of the Truth:** What thoughts, truths, or observations do you want to record today so that they cannot be erased or forgotten?

_____

_____

_____

_____

_____

_____

Day 58

1. **Gratitude Exercise:** What is one extraordinarily beautiful truth about the world that you noticed today?

_____

_____

_____

2. **Examine Your Actions:** Where have you been challenged today? Where have you compromised the truth or fail to live up to the fullness of justice? What are your struggles and challenges living for the sake of Truth?

_____

_____

_____

3. **Resolution for living in Truth & Freedom:** What concrete thing(s) will you do tomorrow to overcome the lies and live more fully in the truth, no matter the cost?

_____

_____

4. **A Daily Record of the Truth:** What thoughts, truths, or observations do you want to record today so that they cannot be erased or forgotten?

_____

_____

_____

_____

_____

_____

Day 59

1. **Gratitude Exercise:** What is one extraordinarily beautiful truth about the world that you noticed today?

_____

_____

_____

2. **Examine Your Actions:** Where have you been challenged today? Where have you compromised the truth or fail to live up to the fullness of justice? What are your struggles and challenges living for the sake of Truth?

_____

_____

_____

3. **Resolution for living in Truth & Freedom:** What concrete thing(s) will you do tomorrow to overcome the lies and live more fully in the truth, no matter the cost?

_____

_____

4. **A Daily Record of the Truth:** What thoughts, truths, or observations do you want to record today so that they cannot be erased or forgotten?

_____

_____

_____

_____

_____

_____

Day 60

1. **Gratitude Exercise:** What is one extraordinarily beautiful truth about the world that you noticed today?

_____

_____

_____

2. **Examine Your Actions:** Where have you been challenged today? Where have you compromised the truth or fail to live up to the fullness of justice? What are your struggles and challenges living for the sake of Truth?

_____

_____

_____

3. **Resolution for living in Truth & Freedom:** What concrete thing(s) will you do tomorrow to overcome the lies and live more fully in the truth, no matter the cost?

_____

_____

4. **A Daily Record of the Truth:** What thoughts, truths, or observations do you want to record today so that they cannot be erased or forgotten?

_____

_____

_____

_____

_____

_____

Day 61

1. **Gratitude Exercise:** What is one extraordinarily beautiful truth about the world that you noticed today?

_____

_____

_____

2. **Examine Your Actions:** Where have you been challenged today? Where have you compromised the truth or fail to live up to the fullness of justice? What are your struggles and challenges living for the sake of Truth?

_____

_____

_____

3. **Resolution for living in Truth & Freedom:** What concrete thing(s) will you do tomorrow to overcome the lies and live more fully in the truth, no matter the cost?

_____

_____

4. **A Daily Record of the Truth:** What thoughts, truths, or observations do you want to record today so that they cannot be erased or forgotten?

_____

_____

_____

_____

_____

_____

Day 62

1. **Gratitude Exercise:** What is one extraordinarily beautiful truth about the world that you noticed today?

   _____

   _____

   _____

2. **Examine Your Actions:** Where have you been challenged today? Where have you compromised the truth or fail to live up to the fullness of justice? What are your struggles and challenges living for the sake of Truth?

   _____

   _____

   _____

3. **Resolution for living in Truth & Freedom:** What concrete thing(s) will you do tomorrow to overcome the lies and live more fully in the truth, no matter the cost?

   _____

   _____

4. **A Daily Record of the Truth:** What thoughts, truths, or observations do you want to record today so that they cannot be erased or forgotten?

   _____

   _____

   _____

   _____

   _____

   _____

Day 63

1. **Gratitude Exercise:** What is one extraordinarily beautiful truth about the world that you noticed today?

_____

_____

_____

2. **Examine Your Actions:** Where have you been challenged today? Where have you compromised the truth or fail to live up to the fullness of justice? What are your struggles and challenges living for the sake of Truth?

_____

_____

_____

3. **Resolution for living in Truth & Freedom:** What concrete thing(s) will you do tomorrow to overcome the lies and live more fully in the truth, no matter the cost?

_____

_____

4. **A Daily Record of the Truth:** What thoughts, truths, or observations do you want to record today so that they cannot be erased or forgotten?

_____

_____

_____

_____

_____

_____

Day 64

1. **Gratitude Exercise:** What is one extraordinarily beautiful truth about the world that you noticed today?

_____

_____

_____

2. **Examine Your Actions:** Where have you been challenged today? Where have you compromised the truth or fail to live up to the fullness of justice? What are your struggles and challenges living for the sake of Truth?

_____

_____

_____

3. **Resolution for living in Truth & Freedom:** What concrete thing(s) will you do tomorrow to overcome the lies and live more fully in the truth, no matter the cost?

_____

_____

4. **A Daily Record of the Truth:** What thoughts, truths, or observations do you want to record today so that they cannot be erased or forgotten?

_____

_____

_____

_____

_____

_____

Day 65

1. **Gratitude Exercise:** What is one extraordinarily beautiful truth about the world that you noticed today?

_____

_____

_____

2. **Examine Your Actions:** Where have you been challenged today? Where have you compromised the truth or fail to live up to the fullness of justice? What are your struggles and challenges living for the sake of Truth?

_____

_____

_____

3. **Resolution for living in Truth & Freedom:** What concrete thing(s) will you do tomorrow to overcome the lies and live more fully in the truth, no matter the cost?

_____

_____

4. **A Daily Record of the Truth:** What thoughts, truths, or observations do you want to record today so that they cannot be erased or forgotten?

_____

_____

_____

_____

_____

_____

Day 66

1. **Gratitude Exercise:** What is one extraordinarily beautiful truth about the world that you noticed today?

    _____

    _____

    _____

2. **Examine Your Actions:** Where have you been challenged today? Where have you compromised the truth or fail to live up to the fullness of justice? What are your struggles and challenges living for the sake of Truth?

    _____

    _____

    _____

3. **Resolution for living in Truth & Freedom:** What concrete thing(s) will you do tomorrow to overcome the lies and live more fully in the truth, no matter the cost?

    _____

    _____

4. **A Daily Record of the Truth:** What thoughts, truths, or observations do you want to record today so that they cannot be erased or forgotten?

    _____

    _____

    _____

    _____

    _____

    _____

Day 67

1. **Gratitude Exercise:** What is one extraordinarily beautiful truth about the world that you noticed today?

_____

_____

_____

2. **Examine Your Actions:** Where have you been challenged today? Where have you compromised the truth or fail to live up to the fullness of justice? What are your struggles and challenges living for the sake of Truth?

_____

_____

_____

3. **Resolution for living in Truth & Freedom:** What concrete thing(s) will you do tomorrow to overcome the lies and live more fully in the truth, no matter the cost?

_____

_____

4. **A Daily Record of the Truth:** What thoughts, truths, or observations do you want to record today so that they cannot be erased or forgotten?

_____

_____

_____

_____

_____

_____

Day 68

1. **Gratitude Exercise:** What is one extraordinarily beautiful truth about the world that you noticed today?

_____

_____

_____

2. **Examine Your Actions:** Where have you been challenged today? Where have you compromised the truth or fail to live up to the fullness of justice? What are your struggles and challenges living for the sake of Truth?

_____

_____

_____

3. **Resolution for living in Truth & Freedom:** What concrete thing(s) will you do tomorrow to overcome the lies and live more fully in the truth, no matter the cost?

_____

_____

4. **A Daily Record of the Truth:** What thoughts, truths, or observations do you want to record today so that they cannot be erased or forgotten?

_____

_____

_____

_____

_____

_____

Day 69

1. **Gratitude Exercise:** What is one extraordinarily beautiful truth about the world that you noticed today?

_____

_____

_____

2. **Examine Your Actions:** Where have you been challenged today? Where have you compromised the truth or fail to live up to the fullness of justice? What are your struggles and challenges living for the sake of Truth?

_____

_____

_____

3. **Resolution for living in Truth & Freedom:** What concrete thing(s) will you do tomorrow to overcome the lies and live more fully in the truth, no matter the cost?

_____

_____

4. **A Daily Record of the Truth:** What thoughts, truths, or observations do you want to record today so that they cannot be erased or forgotten?

_____

_____

_____

_____

_____

_____

Day 70

1. **Gratitude Exercise:** What is one extraordinarily beautiful truth about the world that you noticed today?

_____

_____

_____

2. **Examine Your Actions:** Where have you been challenged today? Where have you compromised the truth or fail to live up to the fullness of justice? What are your struggles and challenges living for the sake of Truth?

_____

_____

_____

3. **Resolution for living in Truth & Freedom:** What concrete thing(s) will you do tomorrow to overcome the lies and live more fully in the truth, no matter the cost?

_____

_____

4. **A Daily Record of the Truth:** What thoughts, truths, or observations do you want to record today so that they cannot be erased or forgotten?

_____

_____

_____

_____

_____

_____

Day 71

1. **Gratitude Exercise:** What is one extraordinarily beautiful truth about the world that you noticed today?

_____

_____

_____

2. **Examine Your Actions:** Where have you been challenged today? Where have you compromised the truth or fail to live up to the fullness of justice? What are your struggles and challenges living for the sake of Truth?

_____

_____

_____

3. **Resolution for living in Truth & Freedom:** What concrete thing(s) will you do tomorrow to overcome the lies and live more fully in the truth, no matter the cost?

_____

_____

4. **A Daily Record of the Truth:** What thoughts, truths, or observations do you want to record today so that they cannot be erased or forgotten?

_____

_____

_____

_____

_____

_____

Day 72

1. **Gratitude Exercise:** What is one extraordinarily beautiful truth about the world that you noticed today?

    _____

    _____

    _____

2. **Examine Your Actions:** Where have you been challenged today? Where have you compromised the truth or fail to live up to the fullness of justice? What are your struggles and challenges living for the sake of Truth?

    _____

    _____

    _____

3. **Resolution for living in Truth & Freedom:** What concrete thing(s) will you do tomorrow to overcome the lies and live more fully in the truth, no matter the cost?

    _____

    _____

4. **A Daily Record of the Truth:** What thoughts, truths, or observations do you want to record today so that they cannot be erased or forgotten?

    _____

    _____

    _____

    _____

    _____

    _____

Day 73

1. **Gratitude Exercise:** What is one extraordinarily beautiful truth about the world that you noticed today?

_____

_____

_____

2. **Examine Your Actions:** Where have you been challenged today? Where have you compromised the truth or fail to live up to the fullness of justice? What are your struggles and challenges living for the sake of Truth?

_____

_____

_____

3. **Resolution for living in Truth & Freedom:** What concrete thing(s) will you do tomorrow to overcome the lies and live more fully in the truth, no matter the cost?

_____

_____

4. **A Daily Record of the Truth:** What thoughts, truths, or observations do you want to record today so that they cannot be erased or forgotten?

_____

_____

_____

_____

_____

_____

Day 74

1. **Gratitude Exercise:** What is one extraordinarily beautiful truth about the world that you noticed today?

_____

_____

_____

2. **Examine Your Actions:** Where have you been challenged today? Where have you compromised the truth or fail to live up to the fullness of justice? What are your struggles and challenges living for the sake of Truth?

_____

_____

_____

3. **Resolution for living in Truth & Freedom:** What concrete thing(s) will you do tomorrow to overcome the lies and live more fully in the truth, no matter the cost?

_____

_____

4. **A Daily Record of the Truth:** What thoughts, truths, or observations do you want to record today so that they cannot be erased or forgotten?

_____

_____

_____

_____

_____

_____

Day 75

1. **Gratitude Exercise:** What is one extraordinarily beautiful truth about the world that you noticed today?

_____

_____

_____

2. **Examine Your Actions:** Where have you been challenged today? Where have you compromised the truth or fail to live up to the fullness of justice? What are your struggles and challenges living for the sake of Truth?

_____

_____

_____

3. **Resolution for living in Truth & Freedom:** What concrete thing(s) will you do tomorrow to overcome the lies and live more fully in the truth, no matter the cost?

_____

_____

4. **A Daily Record of the Truth:** What thoughts, truths, or observations do you want to record today so that they cannot be erased or forgotten?

_____

_____

_____

_____

_____

_____

Day 76

1. **Gratitude Exercise:** What is one extraordinarily beautiful truth about the world that you noticed today?

_____

_____

_____

2. **Examine Your Actions:** Where have you been challenged today? Where have you compromised the truth or fail to live up to the fullness of justice? What are your struggles and challenges living for the sake of Truth?

_____

_____

_____

3. **Resolution for living in Truth & Freedom:** What concrete thing(s) will you do tomorrow to overcome the lies and live more fully in the truth, no matter the cost?

_____

_____

4. **A Daily Record of the Truth:** What thoughts, truths, or observations do you want to record today so that they cannot be erased or forgotten?

_____

_____

_____

_____

_____

_____

Day 77

1. **Gratitude Exercise:** What is one extraordinarily beautiful truth about the world that you noticed today?

_____

_____

_____

2. **Examine Your Actions:** Where have you been challenged today? Where have you compromised the truth or fail to live up to the fullness of justice? What are your struggles and challenges living for the sake of Truth?

_____

_____

_____

3. **Resolution for living in Truth & Freedom:** What concrete thing(s) will you do tomorrow to overcome the lies and live more fully in the truth, no matter the cost?

_____

_____

4. **A Daily Record of the Truth:** What thoughts, truths, or observations do you want to record today so that they cannot be erased or forgotten?

_____

_____

_____

_____

_____

_____

Day 78

1. **Gratitude Exercise:** What is one extraordinarily beautiful truth about the world that you noticed today?

_____

_____

_____

2. **Examine Your Actions:** Where have you been challenged today? Where have you compromised the truth or fail to live up to the fullness of justice? What are your struggles and challenges living for the sake of Truth?

_____

_____

_____

3. **Resolution for living in Truth & Freedom:** What concrete thing(s) will you do tomorrow to overcome the lies and live more fully in the truth, no matter the cost?

_____

_____

4. **A Daily Record of the Truth:** What thoughts, truths, or observations do you want to record today so that they cannot be erased or forgotten?

_____

_____

_____

_____

_____

_____

Day 79

1. **Gratitude Exercise:** What is one extraordinarily beautiful truth about the world that you noticed today?

_____

_____

_____

2. **Examine Your Actions:** Where have you been challenged today? Where have you compromised the truth or fail to live up to the fullness of justice? What are your struggles and challenges living for the sake of Truth?

_____

_____

_____

3. **Resolution for living in Truth & Freedom:** What concrete thing(s) will you do tomorrow to overcome the lies and live more fully in the truth, no matter the cost?

_____

_____

4. **A Daily Record of the Truth:** What thoughts, truths, or observations do you want to record today so that they cannot be erased or forgotten?

_____

_____

_____

_____

_____

Day 80

1. **Gratitude Exercise:** What is one extraordinarily beautiful truth about the world that you noticed today?

_____

_____

_____

2. **Examine Your Actions:** Where have you been challenged today? Where have you compromised the truth or fail to live up to the fullness of justice? What are your struggles and challenges living for the sake of Truth?

_____

_____

_____

3. **Resolution for living in Truth & Freedom:** What concrete thing(s) will you do tomorrow to overcome the lies and live more fully in the truth, no matter the cost?

_____

_____

4. **A Daily Record of the Truth:** What thoughts, truths, or observations do you want to record today so that they cannot be erased or forgotten?

_____

_____

_____

_____

_____

_____

Day 81

1. **Gratitude Exercise:** What is one extraordinarily beautiful truth about the world that you noticed today?

_____

_____

_____

2. **Examine Your Actions:** Where have you been challenged today? Where have you compromised the truth or fail to live up to the fullness of justice? What are your struggles and challenges living for the sake of Truth?

_____

_____

_____

3. **Resolution for living in Truth & Freedom:** What concrete thing(s) will you do tomorrow to overcome the lies and live more fully in the truth, no matter the cost?

_____

_____

4. **A Daily Record of the Truth:** What thoughts, truths, or observations do you want to record today so that they cannot be erased or forgotten?

_____

_____

_____

_____

_____

_____

Day 82

1. **Gratitude Exercise:** What is one extraordinarily beautiful truth about the world that you noticed today?

_____

_____

_____

2. **Examine Your Actions:** Where have you been challenged today? Where have you compromised the truth or fail to live up to the fullness of justice? What are your struggles and challenges living for the sake of Truth?

_____

_____

_____

3. **Resolution for living in Truth & Freedom:** What concrete thing(s) will you do tomorrow to overcome the lies and live more fully in the truth, no matter the cost?

_____

_____

4. **A Daily Record of the Truth:** What thoughts, truths, or observations do you want to record today so that they cannot be erased or forgotten?

_____

_____

_____

_____

_____

_____

Day 83

1. **Gratitude Exercise:** What is one extraordinarily beautiful truth about the world that you noticed today?

_____

_____

_____

2. **Examine Your Actions:** Where have you been challenged today? Where have you compromised the truth or fail to live up to the fullness of justice? What are your struggles and challenges living for the sake of Truth?

_____

_____

_____

3. **Resolution for living in Truth & Freedom:** What concrete thing(s) will you do tomorrow to overcome the lies and live more fully in the truth, no matter the cost?

_____

_____

4. **A Daily Record of the Truth:** What thoughts, truths, or observations do you want to record today so that they cannot be erased or forgotten?

_____

_____

_____

_____

_____

_____

Day 84

1. **Gratitude Exercise:** What is one extraordinarily beautiful truth about the world that you noticed today?

_____

_____

_____

2. **Examine Your Actions:** Where have you been challenged today? Where have you compromised the truth or fail to live up to the fullness of justice? What are your struggles and challenges living for the sake of Truth?

_____

_____

_____

3. **Resolution for living in Truth & Freedom:** What concrete thing(s) will you do tomorrow to overcome the lies and live more fully in the truth, no matter the cost?

_____

_____

4. **A Daily Record of the Truth:** What thoughts, truths, or observations do you want to record today so that they cannot be erased or forgotten?

_____

_____

_____

_____

_____

_____

Day 85

1. **Gratitude Exercise:** What is one extraordinarily beautiful truth about the world that you noticed today?

_____

_____

_____

2. **Examine Your Actions:** Where have you been challenged today? Where have you compromised the truth or fail to live up to the fullness of justice? What are your struggles and challenges living for the sake of Truth?

_____

_____

_____

3. **Resolution for living in Truth & Freedom:** What concrete thing(s) will you do tomorrow to overcome the lies and live more fully in the truth, no matter the cost?

_____

_____

4. **A Daily Record of the Truth:** What thoughts, truths, or observations do you want to record today so that they cannot be erased or forgotten?

_____

_____

_____

_____

_____

_____

Day 86

1. **Gratitude Exercise:** What is one extraordinarily beautiful truth about the world that you noticed today?

_____

_____

_____

2. **Examine Your Actions:** Where have you been challenged today? Where have you compromised the truth or fail to live up to the fullness of justice? What are your struggles and challenges living for the sake of Truth?

_____

_____

_____

3. **Resolution for living in Truth & Freedom:** What concrete thing(s) will you do tomorrow to overcome the lies and live more fully in the truth, no matter the cost?

_____

_____

4. **A Daily Record of the Truth:** What thoughts, truths, or observations do you want to record today so that they cannot be erased or forgotten?

_____

_____

_____

_____

_____

_____

Day 87

1. **Gratitude Exercise:** What is one extraordinarily beautiful truth about the world that you noticed today?

_____

_____

_____

2. **Examine Your Actions:** Where have you been challenged today? Where have you compromised the truth or fail to live up to the fullness of justice? What are your struggles and challenges living for the sake of Truth?

_____

_____

_____

3. **Resolution for living in Truth & Freedom:** What concrete thing(s) will you do tomorrow to overcome the lies and live more fully in the truth, no matter the cost?

_____

_____

4. **A Daily Record of the Truth:** What thoughts, truths, or observations do you want to record today so that they cannot be erased or forgotten?

_____

_____

_____

_____

_____

Day 88

1. **Gratitude Exercise:** What is one extraordinarily beautiful truth about the world that you noticed today?

_____

_____

_____

2. **Examine Your Actions:** Where have you been challenged today? Where have you compromised the truth or fail to live up to the fullness of justice? What are your struggles and challenges living for the sake of Truth?

_____

_____

_____

3. **Resolution for living in Truth & Freedom:** What concrete thing(s) will you do tomorrow to overcome the lies and live more fully in the truth, no matter the cost?

_____

_____

4. **A Daily Record of the Truth:** What thoughts, truths, or observations do you want to record today so that they cannot be erased or forgotten?

_____

_____

_____

_____

_____

_____

Day 89

1. **Gratitude Exercise:** What is one extraordinarily beautiful truth about the world that you noticed today?

_____

_____

_____

2. **Examine Your Actions:** Where have you been challenged today? Where have you compromised the truth or fail to live up to the fullness of justice? What are your struggles and challenges living for the sake of Truth?

_____

_____

_____

3. **Resolution for living in Truth & Freedom:** What concrete thing(s) will you do tomorrow to overcome the lies and live more fully in the truth, no matter the cost?

_____

_____

4. **A Daily Record of the Truth:** What thoughts, truths, or observations do you want to record today so that they cannot be erased or forgotten?

_____

_____

_____

_____

_____

_____

Day 90

1. **Gratitude Exercise:** What is one extraordinarily beautiful truth about the world that you noticed today?

_____

_____

_____

2. **Examine Your Actions:** Where have you been challenged today? Where have you compromised the truth or fail to live up to the fullness of justice? What are your struggles and challenges living for the sake of Truth?

_____

_____

_____

3. **Resolution for living in Truth & Freedom:** What concrete thing(s) will you do tomorrow to overcome the lies and live more fully in the truth, no matter the cost?

_____

_____

4. **A Daily Record of the Truth:** What thoughts, truths, or observations do you want to record today so that they cannot be erased or forgotten?

_____

_____

_____

_____

_____

_____

Day 91

1. **Gratitude Exercise:** What is one extraordinarily beautiful truth about the world that you noticed today?

_____

_____

_____

2. **Examine Your Actions:** Where have you been challenged today? Where have you compromised the truth or fail to live up to the fullness of justice? What are your struggles and challenges living for the sake of Truth?

_____

_____

_____

3. **Resolution for living in Truth & Freedom:** What concrete thing(s) will you do tomorrow to overcome the lies and live more fully in the truth, no matter the cost?

_____

_____

4. **A Daily Record of the Truth:** What thoughts, truths, or observations do you want to record today so that they cannot be erased or forgotten?

_____

_____

_____

_____

_____

Day 92

1. **Gratitude Exercise:** What is one extraordinarily beautiful truth about the world that you noticed today?

_____

_____

_____

2. **Examine Your Actions:** Where have you been challenged today? Where have you compromised the truth or fail to live up to the fullness of justice? What are your struggles and challenges living for the sake of Truth?

_____

_____

_____

3. **Resolution for living in Truth & Freedom:** What concrete thing(s) will you do tomorrow to overcome the lies and live more fully in the truth, no matter the cost?

_____

_____

4. **A Daily Record of the Truth:** What thoughts, truths, or observations do you want to record today so that they cannot be erased or forgotten?

_____

_____

_____

_____

_____

_____

Day 93

1. **Gratitude Exercise:** What is one extraordinarily beautiful truth about the world that you noticed today?

_____

_____

_____

2. **Examine Your Actions:** Where have you been challenged today? Where have you compromised the truth or fail to live up to the fullness of justice? What are your struggles and challenges living for the sake of Truth?

_____

_____

_____

3. **Resolution for living in Truth & Freedom:** What concrete thing(s) will you do tomorrow to overcome the lies and live more fully in the truth, no matter the cost?

_____

_____

4. **A Daily Record of the Truth:** What thoughts, truths, or observations do you want to record today so that they cannot be erased or forgotten?

_____

_____

_____

_____

_____

_____

Day 94

1. **Gratitude Exercise:** What is one extraordinarily beautiful truth about the world that you noticed today?

_____

_____

_____

2. **Examine Your Actions:** Where have you been challenged today? Where have you compromised the truth or fail to live up to the fullness of justice? What are your struggles and challenges living for the sake of Truth?

_____

_____

_____

3. **Resolution for living in Truth & Freedom:** What concrete thing(s) will you do tomorrow to overcome the lies and live more fully in the truth, no matter the cost?

_____

_____

4. **A Daily Record of the Truth:** What thoughts, truths, or observations do you want to record today so that they cannot be erased or forgotten?

_____

_____

_____

_____

_____

_____

Day 95

1. **Gratitude Exercise:** What is one extraordinarily beautiful truth about the world that you noticed today?

_____

_____

_____

2. **Examine Your Actions:** Where have you been challenged today? Where have you compromised the truth or fail to live up to the fullness of justice? What are your struggles and challenges living for the sake of Truth?

_____

_____

_____

3. **Resolution for living in Truth & Freedom:** What concrete thing(s) will you do tomorrow to overcome the lies and live more fully in the truth, no matter the cost?

_____

_____

4. **A Daily Record of the Truth:** What thoughts, truths, or observations do you want to record today so that they cannot be erased or forgotten?

_____

_____

_____

_____

_____

_____

Day 96

1. **Gratitude Exercise:** What is one extraordinarily beautiful truth about the world that you noticed today?

_____

_____

_____

2. **Examine Your Actions:** Where have you been challenged today? Where have you compromised the truth or fail to live up to the fullness of justice? What are your struggles and challenges living for the sake of Truth?

_____

_____

_____

3. **Resolution for living in Truth & Freedom:** What concrete thing(s) will you do tomorrow to overcome the lies and live more fully in the truth, no matter the cost?

_____

_____

4. **A Daily Record of the Truth:** What thoughts, truths, or observations do you want to record today so that they cannot be erased or forgotten?

_____

_____

_____

_____

_____

_____

Day 97

1. **Gratitude Exercise:** What is one extraordinarily beautiful truth about the world that you noticed today?

_____

_____

_____

2. **Examine Your Actions:** Where have you been challenged today? Where have you compromised the truth or fail to live up to the fullness of justice? What are your struggles and challenges living for the sake of Truth?

_____

_____

_____

3. **Resolution for living in Truth & Freedom:** What concrete thing(s) will you do tomorrow to overcome the lies and live more fully in the truth, no matter the cost?

_____

_____

4. **A Daily Record of the Truth:** What thoughts, truths, or observations do you want to record today so that they cannot be erased or forgotten?

_____

_____

_____

_____

_____

Day 98

1. **Gratitude Exercise:** What is one extraordinarily beautiful truth about the world that you noticed today?

_____

_____

_____

2. **Examine Your Actions:** Where have you been challenged today? Where have you compromised the truth or fail to live up to the fullness of justice? What are your struggles and challenges living for the sake of Truth?

_____

_____

_____

3. **Resolution for living in Truth & Freedom:** What concrete thing(s) will you do tomorrow to overcome the lies and live more fully in the truth, no matter the cost?

_____

_____

4. **A Daily Record of the Truth:** What thoughts, truths, or observations do you want to record today so that they cannot be erased or forgotten?

_____

_____

_____

_____

_____

_____

Day 99

1. **Gratitude Exercise:** What is one extraordinarily beautiful truth about the world that you noticed today?

    _____

    _____

    _____

2. **Examine Your Actions:** Where have you been challenged today? Where have you compromised the truth or fail to live up to the fullness of justice? What are your struggles and challenges living for the sake of Truth?

    _____

    _____

    _____

3. **Resolution for living in Truth & Freedom:** What concrete thing(s) will you do tomorrow to overcome the lies and live more fully in the truth, no matter the cost?

    _____

    _____

4. **A Daily Record of the Truth:** What thoughts, truths, or observations do you want to record today so that they cannot be erased or forgotten?

    _____

    _____

    _____

    _____

    _____

    _____

Day 100

1. **Gratitude Exercise:** What is one extraordinarily beautiful truth about the world that you noticed today?

---

2. **Examine Your Actions:** Where have you been challenged today? Where have you compromised the truth or fail to live up to the fullness of justice? What are your struggles and challenges living for the sake of Truth?

---

3. **Resolution for living in Truth & Freedom:** What concrete thing(s) will you do tomorrow to overcome the lies and live more fully in the truth, no matter the cost?

---

4. **A Daily Record of the Truth:** What thoughts, truths, or observations do you want to record today so that they cannot be erased or forgotten?

Day 101

1. **Gratitude Exercise:** What is one extraordinarily beautiful truth about the world that you noticed today?

_____

_____

_____

2. **Examine Your Actions:** Where have you been challenged today? Where have you compromised the truth or fail to live up to the fullness of justice? What are your struggles and challenges living for the sake of Truth?

_____

_____

_____

3. **Resolution for living in Truth & Freedom:** What concrete thing(s) will you do tomorrow to overcome the lies and live more fully in the truth, no matter the cost?

_____

_____

4. **A Daily Record of the Truth:** What thoughts, truths, or observations do you want to record today so that they cannot be erased or forgotten?

_____

_____

_____

_____

_____

_____

Day 102

1. **Gratitude Exercise:** What is one extraordinarily beautiful truth about the world that you noticed today?

   _____

   _____

   _____

2. **Examine Your Actions:** Where have you been challenged today? Where have you compromised the truth or fail to live up to the fullness of justice? What are your struggles and challenges living for the sake of Truth?

   _____

   _____

   _____

3. **Resolution for living in Truth & Freedom:** What concrete thing(s) will you do tomorrow to overcome the lies and live more fully in the truth, no matter the cost?

   _____

   _____

4. **A Daily Record of the Truth:** What thoughts, truths, or observations do you want to record today so that they cannot be erased or forgotten?

   _____

   _____

   _____

   _____

   _____

   _____

Day 103

1. **Gratitude Exercise:** What is one extraordinarily beautiful truth about the world that you noticed today?

_____

_____

_____

2. **Examine Your Actions:** Where have you been challenged today? Where have you compromised the truth or fail to live up to the fullness of justice? What are your struggles and challenges living for the sake of Truth?

_____

_____

_____

3. **Resolution for living in Truth & Freedom:** What concrete thing(s) will you do tomorrow to overcome the lies and live more fully in the truth, no matter the cost?

_____

_____

4. **A Daily Record of the Truth:** What thoughts, truths, or observations do you want to record today so that they cannot be erased or forgotten?

_____

_____

_____

_____

_____

Day 104

1. **Gratitude Exercise:** What is one extraordinarily beautiful truth about the world that you noticed today?

_____

_____

_____

2. **Examine Your Actions:** Where have you been challenged today? Where have you compromised the truth or fail to live up to the fullness of justice? What are your struggles and challenges living for the sake of Truth?

_____

_____

_____

3. **Resolution for living in Truth & Freedom:** What concrete thing(s) will you do tomorrow to overcome the lies and live more fully in the truth, no matter the cost?

_____

_____

4. **A Daily Record of the Truth:** What thoughts, truths, or observations do you want to record today so that they cannot be erased or forgotten?

_____

_____

_____

_____

_____

_____

Day 105

1. **Gratitude Exercise:** What is one extraordinarily beautiful truth about the world that you noticed today?

_____

_____

_____

2. **Examine Your Actions:** Where have you been challenged today? Where have you compromised the truth or fail to live up to the fullness of justice? What are your struggles and challenges living for the sake of Truth?

_____

_____

_____

3. **Resolution for living in Truth & Freedom:** What concrete thing(s) will you do tomorrow to overcome the lies and live more fully in the truth, no matter the cost?

_____

_____

4. **A Daily Record of the Truth:** What thoughts, truths, or observations do you want to record today so that they cannot be erased or forgotten?

_____

_____

_____

_____

_____

_____

Day 106

1. **Gratitude Exercise:** What is one extraordinarily beautiful truth about the world that you noticed today?

_____

_____

_____

2. **Examine Your Actions:** Where have you been challenged today? Where have you compromised the truth or fail to live up to the fullness of justice? What are your struggles and challenges living for the sake of Truth?

_____

_____

_____

3. **Resolution for living in Truth & Freedom:** What concrete thing(s) will you do tomorrow to overcome the lies and live more fully in the truth, no matter the cost?

_____

_____

4. **A Daily Record of the Truth:** What thoughts, truths, or observations do you want to record today so that they cannot be erased or forgotten?

_____

_____

_____

_____

_____

_____

Day 107

1. **Gratitude Exercise:** What is one extraordinarily beautiful truth about the world that you noticed today?

_____

_____

_____

2. **Examine Your Actions:** Where have you been challenged today? Where have you compromised the truth or fail to live up to the fullness of justice? What are your struggles and challenges living for the sake of Truth?

_____

_____

_____

3. **Resolution for living in Truth & Freedom:** What concrete thing(s) will you do tomorrow to overcome the lies and live more fully in the truth, no matter the cost?

_____

_____

4. **A Daily Record of the Truth:** What thoughts, truths, or observations do you want to record today so that they cannot be erased or forgotten?

_____

_____

_____

_____

_____

_____

Day 108

1. **Gratitude Exercise:** What is one extraordinarily beautiful truth about the world that you noticed today?

_____

_____

_____

2. **Examine Your Actions:** Where have you been challenged today? Where have you compromised the truth or fail to live up to the fullness of justice? What are your struggles and challenges living for the sake of Truth?

_____

_____

_____

3. **Resolution for living in Truth & Freedom:** What concrete thing(s) will you do tomorrow to overcome the lies and live more fully in the truth, no matter the cost?

_____

_____

4. **A Daily Record of the Truth:** What thoughts, truths, or observations do you want to record today so that they cannot be erased or forgotten?

_____

_____

_____

_____

_____

_____

Day 109

1. **Gratitude Exercise:** What is one extraordinarily beautiful truth about the world that you noticed today?

_____

_____

_____

2. **Examine Your Actions:** Where have you been challenged today? Where have you compromised the truth or fail to live up to the fullness of justice? What are your struggles and challenges living for the sake of Truth?

_____

_____

_____

3. **Resolution for living in Truth & Freedom:** What concrete thing(s) will you do tomorrow to overcome the lies and live more fully in the truth, no matter the cost?

_____

_____

4. **A Daily Record of the Truth:** What thoughts, truths, or observations do you want to record today so that they cannot be erased or forgotten?

_____

_____

_____

_____

_____

Day 110

1. **Gratitude Exercise:** What is one extraordinarily beautiful truth about the world that you noticed today?

_____

_____

_____

2. **Examine Your Actions:** Where have you been challenged today? Where have you compromised the truth or fail to live up to the fullness of justice? What are your struggles and challenges living for the sake of Truth?

_____

_____

_____

3. **Resolution for living in Truth & Freedom:** What concrete thing(s) will you do tomorrow to overcome the lies and live more fully in the truth, no matter the cost?

_____

_____

4. **A Daily Record of the Truth:** What thoughts, truths, or observations do you want to record today so that they cannot be erased or forgotten?

_____

_____

_____

_____

_____

_____

Day 111

1. **Gratitude Exercise:** What is one extraordinarily beautiful truth about the world that you noticed today?

_____

_____

_____

2. **Examine Your Actions:** Where have you been challenged today? Where have you compromised the truth or fail to live up to the fullness of justice? What are your struggles and challenges living for the sake of Truth?

_____

_____

_____

3. **Resolution for living in Truth & Freedom:** What concrete thing(s) will you do tomorrow to overcome the lies and live more fully in the truth, no matter the cost?

_____

_____

4. **A Daily Record of the Truth:** What thoughts, truths, or observations do you want to record today so that they cannot be erased or forgotten?

_____

_____

_____

_____

_____

_____

Day 112

1. **Gratitude Exercise:** What is one extraordinarily beautiful truth about the world that you noticed today?

_____

_____

_____

2. **Examine Your Actions:** Where have you been challenged today? Where have you compromised the truth or fail to live up to the fullness of justice? What are your struggles and challenges living for the sake of Truth?

_____

_____

_____

3. **Resolution for living in Truth & Freedom:** What concrete thing(s) will you do tomorrow to overcome the lies and live more fully in the truth, no matter the cost?

_____

_____

4. **A Daily Record of the Truth:** What thoughts, truths, or observations do you want to record today so that they cannot be erased or forgotten?

_____

_____

_____

_____

_____

Day 113

1. **Gratitude Exercise:** What is one extraordinarily beautiful truth about the world that you noticed today?

_____

_____

_____

2. **Examine Your Actions:** Where have you been challenged today? Where have you compromised the truth or fail to live up to the fullness of justice? What are your struggles and challenges living for the sake of Truth?

_____

_____

_____

3. **Resolution for living in Truth & Freedom:** What concrete thing(s) will you do tomorrow to overcome the lies and live more fully in the truth, no matter the cost?

_____

_____

4. **A Daily Record of the Truth:** What thoughts, truths, or observations do you want to record today so that they cannot be erased or forgotten?

_____

_____

_____

_____

_____

_____

Day 114

1. **Gratitude Exercise:** What is one extraordinarily beautiful truth about the world that you noticed today?

_____

_____

_____

2. **Examine Your Actions:** Where have you been challenged today? Where have you compromised the truth or fail to live up to the fullness of justice? What are your struggles and challenges living for the sake of Truth?

_____

_____

_____

3. **Resolution for living in Truth & Freedom:** What concrete thing(s) will you do tomorrow to overcome the lies and live more fully in the truth, no matter the cost?

_____

_____

4. **A Daily Record of the Truth:** What thoughts, truths, or observations do you want to record today so that they cannot be erased or forgotten?

_____

_____

_____

_____

_____

_____

Day 115

1. **Gratitude Exercise:** What is one extraordinarily beautiful truth about the world that you noticed today?

_____

_____

_____

2. **Examine Your Actions:** Where have you been challenged today? Where have you compromised the truth or fail to live up to the fullness of justice? What are your struggles and challenges living for the sake of Truth?

_____

_____

_____

3. **Resolution for living in Truth & Freedom:** What concrete thing(s) will you do tomorrow to overcome the lies and live more fully in the truth, no matter the cost?

_____

_____

4. **A Daily Record of the Truth:** What thoughts, truths, or observations do you want to record today so that they cannot be erased or forgotten?

_____

_____

_____

_____

_____

_____

Day 116

1. **Gratitude Exercise:** What is one extraordinarily beautiful truth about the world that you noticed today?

_____

_____

_____

2. **Examine Your Actions:** Where have you been challenged today? Where have you compromised the truth or fail to live up to the fullness of justice? What are your struggles and challenges living for the sake of Truth?

_____

_____

_____

3. **Resolution for living in Truth & Freedom:** What concrete thing(s) will you do tomorrow to overcome the lies and live more fully in the truth, no matter the cost?

_____

_____

4. **A Daily Record of the Truth:** What thoughts, truths, or observations do you want to record today so that they cannot be erased or forgotten?

_____

_____

_____

_____

_____

_____

Day 117

1. **Gratitude Exercise:** What is one extraordinarily beautiful truth about the world that you noticed today?

_____

_____

_____

2. **Examine Your Actions:** Where have you been challenged today? Where have you compromised the truth or fail to live up to the fullness of justice? What are your struggles and challenges living for the sake of Truth?

_____

_____

_____

3. **Resolution for living in Truth & Freedom:** What concrete thing(s) will you do tomorrow to overcome the lies and live more fully in the truth, no matter the cost?

_____

_____

4. **A Daily Record of the Truth:** What thoughts, truths, or observations do you want to record today so that they cannot be erased or forgotten?

_____

_____

_____

_____

_____

_____

Day 118

1. **Gratitude Exercise:** What is one extraordinarily beautiful truth about the world that you noticed today?

   _____

   _____

   _____

2. **Examine Your Actions:** Where have you been challenged today? Where have you compromised the truth or fail to live up to the fullness of justice? What are your struggles and challenges living for the sake of Truth?

   _____

   _____

   _____

3. **Resolution for living in Truth & Freedom:** What concrete thing(s) will you do tomorrow to overcome the lies and live more fully in the truth, no matter the cost?

   _____

   _____

4. **A Daily Record of the Truth:** What thoughts, truths, or observations do you want to record today so that they cannot be erased or forgotten?

   _____

   _____

   _____

   _____

   _____

   _____

Day 119

1. **Gratitude Exercise:** What is one extraordinarily beautiful truth about the world that you noticed today?

_____

_____

_____

2. **Examine Your Actions:** Where have you been challenged today? Where have you compromised the truth or fail to live up to the fullness of justice? What are your struggles and challenges living for the sake of Truth?

_____

_____

_____

3. **Resolution for living in Truth & Freedom:** What concrete thing(s) will you do tomorrow to overcome the lies and live more fully in the truth, no matter the cost?

_____

_____

4. **A Daily Record of the Truth:** What thoughts, truths, or observations do you want to record today so that they cannot be erased or forgotten?

_____

_____

_____

_____

_____

_____

Day 120

1. **Gratitude Exercise:** What is one extraordinarily beautiful truth about the world that you noticed today?

_____

_____

_____

2. **Examine Your Actions:** Where have you been challenged today? Where have you compromised the truth or fail to live up to the fullness of justice? What are your struggles and challenges living for the sake of Truth?

_____

_____

_____

3. **Resolution for living in Truth & Freedom:** What concrete thing(s) will you do tomorrow to overcome the lies and live more fully in the truth, no matter the cost?

_____

_____

4. **A Daily Record of the Truth:** What thoughts, truths, or observations do you want to record today so that they cannot be erased or forgotten?

_____

_____

_____

_____

_____

_____

Day 121

1. **Gratitude Exercise:** What is one extraordinarily beautiful truth about the world that you noticed today?

_____

_____

_____

2. **Examine Your Actions:** Where have you been challenged today? Where have you compromised the truth or fail to live up to the fullness of justice? What are your struggles and challenges living for the sake of Truth?

_____

_____

_____

3. **Resolution for living in Truth & Freedom:** What concrete thing(s) will you do tomorrow to overcome the lies and live more fully in the truth, no matter the cost?

_____

_____

4. **A Daily Record of the Truth:** What thoughts, truths, or observations do you want to record today so that they cannot be erased or forgotten?

_____

_____

_____

_____

_____

_____

Day 122

1. **Gratitude Exercise:** What is one extraordinarily beautiful truth about the world that you noticed today?

    _____

    _____

    _____

2. **Examine Your Actions:** Where have you been challenged today? Where have you compromised the truth or fail to live up to the fullness of justice? What are your struggles and challenges living for the sake of Truth?

    _____

    _____

    _____

3. **Resolution for living in Truth & Freedom:** What concrete thing(s) will you do tomorrow to overcome the lies and live more fully in the truth, no matter the cost?

    _____

    _____

4. **A Daily Record of the Truth:** What thoughts, truths, or observations do you want to record today so that they cannot be erased or forgotten?

    _____

    _____

    _____

    _____

    _____

Day 123

1. **Gratitude Exercise:** What is one extraordinarily beautiful truth about the world that you noticed today?

_____

_____

_____

2. **Examine Your Actions:** Where have you been challenged today? Where have you compromised the truth or fail to live up to the fullness of justice? What are your struggles and challenges living for the sake of Truth?

_____

_____

_____

3. **Resolution for living in Truth & Freedom:** What concrete thing(s) will you do tomorrow to overcome the lies and live more fully in the truth, no matter the cost?

_____

_____

4. **A Daily Record of the Truth:** What thoughts, truths, or observations do you want to record today so that they cannot be erased or forgotten?

_____

_____

_____

_____

_____

_____

Day 124

1. **Gratitude Exercise:** What is one extraordinarily beautiful truth about the world that you noticed today?

   _____

   _____

   _____

2. **Examine Your Actions:** Where have you been challenged today? Where have you compromised the truth or fail to live up to the fullness of justice? What are your struggles and challenges living for the sake of Truth?

   _____

   _____

   _____

3. **Resolution for living in Truth & Freedom:** What concrete thing(s) will you do tomorrow to overcome the lies and live more fully in the truth, no matter the cost?

   _____

   _____

4. **A Daily Record of the Truth:** What thoughts, truths, or observations do you want to record today so that they cannot be erased or forgotten?

   _____

   _____

   _____

   _____

   _____

   _____

Day 125

1. **Gratitude Exercise:** What is one extraordinarily beautiful truth about the world that you noticed today?

_____

_____

_____

2. **Examine Your Actions:** Where have you been challenged today? Where have you compromised the truth or fail to live up to the fullness of justice? What are your struggles and challenges living for the sake of Truth?

_____

_____

_____

3. **Resolution for living in Truth & Freedom:** What concrete thing(s) will you do tomorrow to overcome the lies and live more fully in the truth, no matter the cost?

_____

_____

4. **A Daily Record of the Truth:** What thoughts, truths, or observations do you want to record today so that they cannot be erased or forgotten?

_____

_____

_____

_____

_____

_____

Day 126

1. **Gratitude Exercise:** What is one extraordinarily beautiful truth about the world that you noticed today?

_____

_____

_____

2. **Examine Your Actions:** Where have you been challenged today? Where have you compromised the truth or fail to live up to the fullness of justice? What are your struggles and challenges living for the sake of Truth?

_____

_____

_____

3. **Resolution for living in Truth & Freedom:** What concrete thing(s) will you do tomorrow to overcome the lies and live more fully in the truth, no matter the cost?

_____

_____

4. **A Daily Record of the Truth:** What thoughts, truths, or observations do you want to record today so that they cannot be erased or forgotten?

_____

_____

_____

_____

_____

Day 127

1. **Gratitude Exercise:** What is one extraordinarily beautiful truth about the world that you noticed today?

_____

_____

_____

2. **Examine Your Actions:** Where have you been challenged today? Where have you compromised the truth or fail to live up to the fullness of justice? What are your struggles and challenges living for the sake of Truth?

_____

_____

_____

3. **Resolution for living in Truth & Freedom:** What concrete thing(s) will you do tomorrow to overcome the lies and live more fully in the truth, no matter the cost?

_____

_____

4. **A Daily Record of the Truth:** What thoughts, truths, or observations do you want to record today so that they cannot be erased or forgotten?

_____

_____

_____

_____

_____

_____

Day 128

1. **Gratitude Exercise:** What is one extraordinarily beautiful truth about the world that you noticed today?

_____

_____

_____

2. **Examine Your Actions:** Where have you been challenged today? Where have you compromised the truth or fail to live up to the fullness of justice? What are your struggles and challenges living for the sake of Truth?

_____

_____

_____

3. **Resolution for living in Truth & Freedom:** What concrete thing(s) will you do tomorrow to overcome the lies and live more fully in the truth, no matter the cost?

_____

_____

4. **A Daily Record of the Truth:** What thoughts, truths, or observations do you want to record today so that they cannot be erased or forgotten?

_____

_____

_____

_____

_____

_____

Day 129

1. **Gratitude Exercise:** What is one extraordinarily beautiful truth about the world that you noticed today?

_____

_____

_____

2. **Examine Your Actions:** Where have you been challenged today? Where have you compromised the truth or fail to live up to the fullness of justice? What are your struggles and challenges living for the sake of Truth?

_____

_____

_____

3. **Resolution for living in Truth & Freedom:** What concrete thing(s) will you do tomorrow to overcome the lies and live more fully in the truth, no matter the cost?

_____

_____

4. **A Daily Record of the Truth:** What thoughts, truths, or observations do you want to record today so that they cannot be erased or forgotten?

_____

_____

_____

_____

_____

_____

Day 130

1. **Gratitude Exercise:** What is one extraordinarily beautiful truth about the world that you noticed today?

_____

_____

_____

2. **Examine Your Actions:** Where have you been challenged today? Where have you compromised the truth or fail to live up to the fullness of justice? What are your struggles and challenges living for the sake of Truth?

_____

_____

_____

3. **Resolution for living in Truth & Freedom:** What concrete thing(s) will you do tomorrow to overcome the lies and live more fully in the truth, no matter the cost?

_____

_____

4. **A Daily Record of the Truth:** What thoughts, truths, or observations do you want to record today so that they cannot be erased or forgotten?

_____

_____

_____

_____

_____

_____

Day 131

1. **Gratitude Exercise:** What is one extraordinarily beautiful truth about the world that you noticed today?

_____

_____

_____

2. **Examine Your Actions:** Where have you been challenged today? Where have you compromised the truth or fail to live up to the fullness of justice? What are your struggles and challenges living for the sake of Truth?

_____

_____

_____

3. **Resolution for living in Truth & Freedom:** What concrete thing(s) will you do tomorrow to overcome the lies and live more fully in the truth, no matter the cost?

_____

_____

4. **A Daily Record of the Truth:** What thoughts, truths, or observations do you want to record today so that they cannot be erased or forgotten?

_____

_____

_____

_____

_____

_____

Day 132

1. **Gratitude Exercise:** What is one extraordinarily beautiful truth about the world that you noticed today?

_____

_____

_____

2. **Examine Your Actions:** Where have you been challenged today? Where have you compromised the truth or fail to live up to the fullness of justice? What are your struggles and challenges living for the sake of Truth?

_____

_____

_____

3. **Resolution for living in Truth & Freedom:** What concrete thing(s) will you do tomorrow to overcome the lies and live more fully in the truth, no matter the cost?

_____

_____

4. **A Daily Record of the Truth:** What thoughts, truths, or observations do you want to record today so that they cannot be erased or forgotten?

_____

_____

_____

_____

_____

_____

Day 133

1. **Gratitude Exercise:** What is one extraordinarily beautiful truth about the world that you noticed today?

_____

_____

_____

2. **Examine Your Actions:** Where have you been challenged today? Where have you compromised the truth or fail to live up to the fullness of justice? What are your struggles and challenges living for the sake of Truth?

_____

_____

_____

3. **Resolution for living in Truth & Freedom:** What concrete thing(s) will you do tomorrow to overcome the lies and live more fully in the truth, no matter the cost?

_____

_____

4. **A Daily Record of the Truth:** What thoughts, truths, or observations do you want to record today so that they cannot be erased or forgotten?

_____

_____

_____

_____

_____

_____

Day 134

1. **Gratitude Exercise:** What is one extraordinarily beautiful truth about the world that you noticed today?

   _____

   _____

   _____

2. **Examine Your Actions:** Where have you been challenged today? Where have you compromised the truth or fail to live up to the fullness of justice? What are your struggles and challenges living for the sake of Truth?

   _____

   _____

   _____

3. **Resolution for living in Truth & Freedom:** What concrete thing(s) will you do tomorrow to overcome the lies and live more fully in the truth, no matter the cost?

   _____

   _____

4. **A Daily Record of the Truth:** What thoughts, truths, or observations do you want to record today so that they cannot be erased or forgotten?

   _____

   _____

   _____

   _____

   _____

   _____

Day 135

1. **Gratitude Exercise:** What is one extraordinarily beautiful truth about the world that you noticed today?

_____

_____

_____

2. **Examine Your Actions:** Where have you been challenged today? Where have you compromised the truth or fail to live up to the fullness of justice? What are your struggles and challenges living for the sake of Truth?

_____

_____

_____

3. **Resolution for living in Truth & Freedom:** What concrete thing(s) will you do tomorrow to overcome the lies and live more fully in the truth, no matter the cost?

_____

_____

4. **A Daily Record of the Truth:** What thoughts, truths, or observations do you want to record today so that they cannot be erased or forgotten?

_____

_____

_____

_____

_____

_____

Day 136

1. **Gratitude Exercise:** What is one extraordinarily beautiful truth about the world that you noticed today?

_____

_____

_____

2. **Examine Your Actions:** Where have you been challenged today? Where have you compromised the truth or fail to live up to the fullness of justice? What are your struggles and challenges living for the sake of Truth?

_____

_____

_____

3. **Resolution for living in Truth & Freedom:** What concrete thing(s) will you do tomorrow to overcome the lies and live more fully in the truth, no matter the cost?

_____

_____

4. **A Daily Record of the Truth:** What thoughts, truths, or observations do you want to record today so that they cannot be erased or forgotten?

_____

_____

_____

_____

_____

Day 137

1. **Gratitude Exercise:** What is one extraordinarily beautiful truth about the world that you noticed today?

_____

_____

_____

2. **Examine Your Actions:** Where have you been challenged today? Where have you compromised the truth or fail to live up to the fullness of justice? What are your struggles and challenges living for the sake of Truth?

_____

_____

_____

3. **Resolution for living in Truth & Freedom:** What concrete thing(s) will you do tomorrow to overcome the lies and live more fully in the truth, no matter the cost?

_____

_____

4. **A Daily Record of the Truth:** What thoughts, truths, or observations do you want to record today so that they cannot be erased or forgotten?

_____

_____

_____

_____

_____

_____

Day 138

1. **Gratitude Exercise:** What is one extraordinarily beautiful truth about the world that you noticed today?

_____

_____

_____

2. **Examine Your Actions:** Where have you been challenged today? Where have you compromised the truth or fail to live up to the fullness of justice? What are your struggles and challenges living for the sake of Truth?

_____

_____

_____

3. **Resolution for living in Truth & Freedom:** What concrete thing(s) will you do tomorrow to overcome the lies and live more fully in the truth, no matter the cost?

_____

_____

4. **A Daily Record of the Truth:** What thoughts, truths, or observations do you want to record today so that they cannot be erased or forgotten?

_____

_____

_____

_____

_____

_____

Day 139

1. **Gratitude Exercise:** What is one extraordinarily beautiful truth about the world that you noticed today?

_____

_____

_____

2. **Examine Your Actions:** Where have you been challenged today? Where have you compromised the truth or fail to live up to the fullness of justice? What are your struggles and challenges living for the sake of Truth?

_____

_____

_____

3. **Resolution for living in Truth & Freedom:** What concrete thing(s) will you do tomorrow to overcome the lies and live more fully in the truth, no matter the cost?

_____

_____

4. **A Daily Record of the Truth:** What thoughts, truths, or observations do you want to record today so that they cannot be erased or forgotten?

_____

_____

_____

_____

_____

_____

Day 140

1. **Gratitude Exercise:** What is one extraordinarily beautiful truth about the world that you noticed today?

_____

_____

_____

2. **Examine Your Actions:** Where have you been challenged today? Where have you compromised the truth or fail to live up to the fullness of justice? What are your struggles and challenges living for the sake of Truth?

_____

_____

_____

3. **Resolution for living in Truth & Freedom:** What concrete thing(s) will you do tomorrow to overcome the lies and live more fully in the truth, no matter the cost?

_____

_____

4. **A Daily Record of the Truth:** What thoughts, truths, or observations do you want to record today so that they cannot be erased or forgotten?

_____

_____

_____

_____

_____

Day 141

1. **Gratitude Exercise:** What is one extraordinarily beautiful truth about the world that you noticed today?

_____

_____

_____

2. **Examine Your Actions:** Where have you been challenged today? Where have you compromised the truth or fail to live up to the fullness of justice? What are your struggles and challenges living for the sake of Truth?

_____

_____

_____

3. **Resolution for living in Truth & Freedom:** What concrete thing(s) will you do tomorrow to overcome the lies and live more fully in the truth, no matter the cost?

_____

_____

4. **A Daily Record of the Truth:** What thoughts, truths, or observations do you want to record today so that they cannot be erased or forgotten?

_____

_____

_____

_____

_____

_____

Day 142

1. **Gratitude Exercise:** What is one extraordinarily beautiful truth about the world that you noticed today?

_____

_____

_____

2. **Examine Your Actions:** Where have you been challenged today? Where have you compromised the truth or fail to live up to the fullness of justice? What are your struggles and challenges living for the sake of Truth?

_____

_____

_____

3. **Resolution for living in Truth & Freedom:** What concrete thing(s) will you do tomorrow to overcome the lies and live more fully in the truth, no matter the cost?

_____

_____

4. **A Daily Record of the Truth:** What thoughts, truths, or observations do you want to record today so that they cannot be erased or forgotten?

_____

_____

_____

_____

_____

_____

Day 143

1. **Gratitude Exercise:** What is one extraordinarily beautiful truth about the world that you noticed today?

_____

_____

_____

2. **Examine Your Actions:** Where have you been challenged today? Where have you compromised the truth or fail to live up to the fullness of justice? What are your struggles and challenges living for the sake of Truth?

_____

_____

_____

3. **Resolution for living in Truth & Freedom:** What concrete thing(s) will you do tomorrow to overcome the lies and live more fully in the truth, no matter the cost?

_____

_____

4. **A Daily Record of the Truth:** What thoughts, truths, or observations do you want to record today so that they cannot be erased or forgotten?

_____

_____

_____

_____

_____

Day 144

1. **Gratitude Exercise:** What is one extraordinarily beautiful truth about the world that you noticed today?

_____

_____

_____

2. **Examine Your Actions:** Where have you been challenged today? Where have you compromised the truth or fail to live up to the fullness of justice? What are your struggles and challenges living for the sake of Truth?

_____

_____

_____

3. **Resolution for living in Truth & Freedom:** What concrete thing(s) will you do tomorrow to overcome the lies and live more fully in the truth, no matter the cost?

_____

_____

4. **A Daily Record of the Truth:** What thoughts, truths, or observations do you want to record today so that they cannot be erased or forgotten?

_____

_____

_____

_____

_____

_____

Day 145

1. **Gratitude Exercise:** What is one extraordinarily beautiful truth about the world that you noticed today?

_____

_____

_____

2. **Examine Your Actions:** Where have you been challenged today? Where have you compromised the truth or fail to live up to the fullness of justice? What are your struggles and challenges living for the sake of Truth?

_____

_____

_____

3. **Resolution for living in Truth & Freedom:** What concrete thing(s) will you do tomorrow to overcome the lies and live more fully in the truth, no matter the cost?

_____

_____

4. **A Daily Record of the Truth:** What thoughts, truths, or observations do you want to record today so that they cannot be erased or forgotten?

_____

_____

_____

_____

_____

_____

Day 146

1. **Gratitude Exercise:** What is one extraordinarily beautiful truth about the world that you noticed today?

_____

_____

_____

2. **Examine Your Actions:** Where have you been challenged today? Where have you compromised the truth or fail to live up to the fullness of justice? What are your struggles and challenges living for the sake of Truth?

_____

_____

_____

3. **Resolution for living in Truth & Freedom:** What concrete thing(s) will you do tomorrow to overcome the lies and live more fully in the truth, no matter the cost?

_____

_____

4. **A Daily Record of the Truth:** What thoughts, truths, or observations do you want to record today so that they cannot be erased or forgotten?

_____

_____

_____

_____

_____

_____

Day 147

1. **Gratitude Exercise:** What is one extraordinarily beautiful truth about the world that you noticed today?

_____

_____

_____

2. **Examine Your Actions:** Where have you been challenged today? Where have you compromised the truth or fail to live up to the fullness of justice? What are your struggles and challenges living for the sake of Truth?

_____

_____

_____

3. **Resolution for living in Truth & Freedom:** What concrete thing(s) will you do tomorrow to overcome the lies and live more fully in the truth, no matter the cost?

_____

_____

4. **A Daily Record of the Truth:** What thoughts, truths, or observations do you want to record today so that they cannot be erased or forgotten?

_____

_____

_____

_____

_____

Day 148

1. **Gratitude Exercise:** What is one extraordinarily beautiful truth about the world that you noticed today?

   _____

   _____

   _____

2. **Examine Your Actions:** Where have you been challenged today? Where have you compromised the truth or fail to live up to the fullness of justice? What are your struggles and challenges living for the sake of Truth?

   _____

   _____

   _____

3. **Resolution for living in Truth & Freedom:** What concrete thing(s) will you do tomorrow to overcome the lies and live more fully in the truth, no matter the cost?

   _____

   _____

4. **A Daily Record of the Truth:** What thoughts, truths, or observations do you want to record today so that they cannot be erased or forgotten?

   _____

   _____

   _____

   _____

   _____

   _____

Day 149

1. **Gratitude Exercise:** What is one extraordinarily beautiful truth about the world that you noticed today?

_____

_____

_____

2. **Examine Your Actions:** Where have you been challenged today? Where have you compromised the truth or fail to live up to the fullness of justice? What are your struggles and challenges living for the sake of Truth?

_____

_____

_____

3. **Resolution for living in Truth & Freedom:** What concrete thing(s) will you do tomorrow to overcome the lies and live more fully in the truth, no matter the cost?

_____

_____

4. **A Daily Record of the Truth:** What thoughts, truths, or observations do you want to record today so that they cannot be erased or forgotten?

_____

_____

_____

_____

_____

Day 150

1. **Gratitude Exercise:** What is one extraordinarily beautiful truth about the world that you noticed today?

_____

_____

_____

2. **Examine Your Actions:** Where have you been challenged today? Where have you compromised the truth or fail to live up to the fullness of justice? What are your struggles and challenges living for the sake of Truth?

_____

_____

_____

3. **Resolution for living in Truth & Freedom:** What concrete thing(s) will you do tomorrow to overcome the lies and live more fully in the truth, no matter the cost?

_____

_____

4. **A Daily Record of the Truth:** What thoughts, truths, or observations do you want to record today so that they cannot be erased or forgotten?

_____

_____

_____

_____

_____

_____

Day 151

1. **Gratitude Exercise:** What is one extraordinarily beautiful truth about the world that you noticed today?

_____

_____

_____

2. **Examine Your Actions:** Where have you been challenged today? Where have you compromised the truth or fail to live up to the fullness of justice? What are your struggles and challenges living for the sake of Truth?

_____

_____

_____

3. **Resolution for living in Truth & Freedom:** What concrete thing(s) will you do tomorrow to overcome the lies and live more fully in the truth, no matter the cost?

_____

_____

4. **A Daily Record of the Truth:** What thoughts, truths, or observations do you want to record today so that they cannot be erased or forgotten?

_____

_____

_____

_____

_____

_____

Day 152

1. **Gratitude Exercise:** What is one extraordinarily beautiful truth about the world that you noticed today?

_____

_____

_____

2. **Examine Your Actions:** Where have you been challenged today? Where have you compromised the truth or fail to live up to the fullness of justice? What are your struggles and challenges living for the sake of Truth?

_____

_____

_____

3. **Resolution for living in Truth & Freedom:** What concrete thing(s) will you do tomorrow to overcome the lies and live more fully in the truth, no matter the cost?

_____

_____

4. **A Daily Record of the Truth:** What thoughts, truths, or observations do you want to record today so that they cannot be erased or forgotten?

_____

_____

_____

_____

_____

_____

Day 153

1. **Gratitude Exercise:** What is one extraordinarily beautiful truth about the world that you noticed today?

_____

_____

_____

2. **Examine Your Actions:** Where have you been challenged today? Where have you compromised the truth or fail to live up to the fullness of justice? What are your struggles and challenges living for the sake of Truth?

_____

_____

_____

3. **Resolution for living in Truth & Freedom:** What concrete thing(s) will you do tomorrow to overcome the lies and live more fully in the truth, no matter the cost?

_____

_____

4. **A Daily Record of the Truth:** What thoughts, truths, or observations do you want to record today so that they cannot be erased or forgotten?

_____

_____

_____

_____

_____

_____

Day 154

1. **Gratitude Exercise:** What is one extraordinarily beautiful truth about the world that you noticed today?

   _____

   _____

   _____

2. **Examine Your Actions:** Where have you been challenged today? Where have you compromised the truth or fail to live up to the fullness of justice? What are your struggles and challenges living for the sake of Truth?

   _____

   _____

   _____

3. **Resolution for living in Truth & Freedom:** What concrete thing(s) will you do tomorrow to overcome the lies and live more fully in the truth, no matter the cost?

   _____

   _____

4. **A Daily Record of the Truth:** What thoughts, truths, or observations do you want to record today so that they cannot be erased or forgotten?

   _____

   _____

   _____

   _____

   _____

   _____

Day 155

1. **Gratitude Exercise:** What is one extraordinarily beautiful truth about the world that you noticed today?

_____

_____

_____

2. **Examine Your Actions:** Where have you been challenged today? Where have you compromised the truth or fail to live up to the fullness of justice? What are your struggles and challenges living for the sake of Truth?

_____

_____

_____

3. **Resolution for living in Truth & Freedom:** What concrete thing(s) will you do tomorrow to overcome the lies and live more fully in the truth, no matter the cost?

_____

_____

4. **A Daily Record of the Truth:** What thoughts, truths, or observations do you want to record today so that they cannot be erased or forgotten?

_____

_____

_____

_____

_____

_____

Day 156

1. **Gratitude Exercise:** What is one extraordinarily beautiful truth about the world that you noticed today?

_____

_____

_____

2. **Examine Your Actions:** Where have you been challenged today? Where have you compromised the truth or fail to live up to the fullness of justice? What are your struggles and challenges living for the sake of Truth?

_____

_____

_____

3. **Resolution for living in Truth & Freedom:** What concrete thing(s) will you do tomorrow to overcome the lies and live more fully in the truth, no matter the cost?

_____

_____

4. **A Daily Record of the Truth:** What thoughts, truths, or observations do you want to record today so that they cannot be erased or forgotten?

_____

_____

_____

_____

_____

_____

Day 157

1. **Gratitude Exercise:** What is one extraordinarily beautiful truth about the world that you noticed today?

_____

_____

_____

2. **Examine Your Actions:** Where have you been challenged today? Where have you compromised the truth or fail to live up to the fullness of justice? What are your struggles and challenges living for the sake of Truth?

_____

_____

_____

3. **Resolution for living in Truth & Freedom:** What concrete thing(s) will you do tomorrow to overcome the lies and live more fully in the truth, no matter the cost?

_____

_____

4. **A Daily Record of the Truth:** What thoughts, truths, or observations do you want to record today so that they cannot be erased or forgotten?

_____

_____

_____

_____

_____

_____

Day 158

1. **Gratitude Exercise:** What is one extraordinarily beautiful truth about the world that you noticed today?

_____

_____

_____

2. **Examine Your Actions:** Where have you been challenged today? Where have you compromised the truth or fail to live up to the fullness of justice? What are your struggles and challenges living for the sake of Truth?

_____

_____

_____

3. **Resolution for living in Truth & Freedom:** What concrete thing(s) will you do tomorrow to overcome the lies and live more fully in the truth, no matter the cost?

_____

_____

4. **A Daily Record of the Truth:** What thoughts, truths, or observations do you want to record today so that they cannot be erased or forgotten?

_____

_____

_____

_____

_____

Day 159

1. **Gratitude Exercise:** What is one extraordinarily beautiful truth about the world that you noticed today?

_____

_____

_____

2. **Examine Your Actions:** Where have you been challenged today? Where have you compromised the truth or fail to live up to the fullness of justice? What are your struggles and challenges living for the sake of Truth?

_____

_____

_____

3. **Resolution for living in Truth & Freedom:** What concrete thing(s) will you do tomorrow to overcome the lies and live more fully in the truth, no matter the cost?

_____

_____

4. **A Daily Record of the Truth:** What thoughts, truths, or observations do you want to record today so that they cannot be erased or forgotten?

_____

_____

_____

_____

_____

_____

Day 160

1. **Gratitude Exercise:** What is one extraordinarily beautiful truth about the world that you noticed today?

_____

_____

_____

2. **Examine Your Actions:** Where have you been challenged today? Where have you compromised the truth or fail to live up to the fullness of justice? What are your struggles and challenges living for the sake of Truth?

_____

_____

_____

3. **Resolution for living in Truth & Freedom:** What concrete thing(s) will you do tomorrow to overcome the lies and live more fully in the truth, no matter the cost?

_____

_____

4. **A Daily Record of the Truth:** What thoughts, truths, or observations do you want to record today so that they cannot be erased or forgotten?

_____

_____

_____

_____

_____

_____

Day 161

1. **Gratitude Exercise:** What is one extraordinarily beautiful truth about the world that you noticed today?

_____

_____

_____

2. **Examine Your Actions:** Where have you been challenged today? Where have you compromised the truth or fail to live up to the fullness of justice? What are your struggles and challenges living for the sake of Truth?

_____

_____

_____

3. **Resolution for living in Truth & Freedom:** What concrete thing(s) will you do tomorrow to overcome the lies and live more fully in the truth, no matter the cost?

_____

_____

4. **A Daily Record of the Truth:** What thoughts, truths, or observations do you want to record today so that they cannot be erased or forgotten?

_____

_____

_____

_____

_____

_____

Day 162

1. **Gratitude Exercise:** What is one extraordinarily beautiful truth about the world that you noticed today?

_____

_____

_____

2. **Examine Your Actions:** Where have you been challenged today? Where have you compromised the truth or fail to live up to the fullness of justice? What are your struggles and challenges living for the sake of Truth?

_____

_____

_____

3. **Resolution for living in Truth & Freedom:** What concrete thing(s) will you do tomorrow to overcome the lies and live more fully in the truth, no matter the cost?

_____

_____

4. **A Daily Record of the Truth:** What thoughts, truths, or observations do you want to record today so that they cannot be erased or forgotten?

_____

_____

_____

_____

_____

_____

Day 163

1. **Gratitude Exercise:** What is one extraordinarily beautiful truth about the world that you noticed today?

_____

_____

_____

2. **Examine Your Actions:** Where have you been challenged today? Where have you compromised the truth or fail to live up to the fullness of justice? What are your struggles and challenges living for the sake of Truth?

_____

_____

_____

3. **Resolution for living in Truth & Freedom:** What concrete thing(s) will you do tomorrow to overcome the lies and live more fully in the truth, no matter the cost?

_____

_____

4. **A Daily Record of the Truth:** What thoughts, truths, or observations do you want to record today so that they cannot be erased or forgotten?

_____

_____

_____

_____

_____

Day 164

1. **Gratitude Exercise:** What is one extraordinarily beautiful truth about the world that you noticed today?

_____

_____

_____

2. **Examine Your Actions:** Where have you been challenged today? Where have you compromised the truth or fail to live up to the fullness of justice? What are your struggles and challenges living for the sake of Truth?

_____

_____

_____

3. **Resolution for living in Truth & Freedom:** What concrete thing(s) will you do tomorrow to overcome the lies and live more fully in the truth, no matter the cost?

_____

_____

4. **A Daily Record of the Truth:** What thoughts, truths, or observations do you want to record today so that they cannot be erased or forgotten?

_____

_____

_____

_____

_____

_____

Day 165

1. **Gratitude Exercise:** What is one extraordinarily beautiful truth about the world that you noticed today?

_____

_____

_____

2. **Examine Your Actions:** Where have you been challenged today? Where have you compromised the truth or fail to live up to the fullness of justice? What are your struggles and challenges living for the sake of Truth?

_____

_____

_____

3. **Resolution for living in Truth & Freedom:** What concrete thing(s) will you do tomorrow to overcome the lies and live more fully in the truth, no matter the cost?

_____

_____

4. **A Daily Record of the Truth:** What thoughts, truths, or observations do you want to record today so that they cannot be erased or forgotten?

_____

_____

_____

_____

_____

_____

Day 166

1. **Gratitude Exercise:** What is one extraordinarily beautiful truth about the world that you noticed today?

    _____

    _____

    _____

2. **Examine Your Actions:** Where have you been challenged today? Where have you compromised the truth or fail to live up to the fullness of justice? What are your struggles and challenges living for the sake of Truth?

    _____

    _____

    _____

3. **Resolution for living in Truth & Freedom:** What concrete thing(s) will you do tomorrow to overcome the lies and live more fully in the truth, no matter the cost?

    _____

    _____

4. **A Daily Record of the Truth:** What thoughts, truths, or observations do you want to record today so that they cannot be erased or forgotten?

    _____

    _____

    _____

    _____

    _____

    _____

Day 167

1. **Gratitude Exercise:** What is one extraordinarily beautiful truth about the world that you noticed today?

_____

_____

_____

2. **Examine Your Actions:** Where have you been challenged today? Where have you compromised the truth or fail to live up to the fullness of justice? What are your struggles and challenges living for the sake of Truth?

_____

_____

_____

3. **Resolution for living in Truth & Freedom:** What concrete thing(s) will you do tomorrow to overcome the lies and live more fully in the truth, no matter the cost?

_____

_____

4. **A Daily Record of the Truth:** What thoughts, truths, or observations do you want to record today so that they cannot be erased or forgotten?

_____

_____

_____

_____

_____

Day 168

1. **Gratitude Exercise:** What is one extraordinarily beautiful truth about the world that you noticed today?

_____

_____

_____

2. **Examine Your Actions:** Where have you been challenged today? Where have you compromised the truth or fail to live up to the fullness of justice? What are your struggles and challenges living for the sake of Truth?

_____

_____

_____

3. **Resolution for living in Truth & Freedom:** What concrete thing(s) will you do tomorrow to overcome the lies and live more fully in the truth, no matter the cost?

_____

_____

4. **A Daily Record of the Truth:** What thoughts, truths, or observations do you want to record today so that they cannot be erased or forgotten?

_____

_____

_____

_____

_____

Day 169

1. **Gratitude Exercise:** What is one extraordinarily beautiful truth about the world that you noticed today?

_____

_____

_____

2. **Examine Your Actions:** Where have you been challenged today? Where have you compromised the truth or fail to live up to the fullness of justice? What are your struggles and challenges living for the sake of Truth?

_____

_____

_____

3. **Resolution for living in Truth & Freedom:** What concrete thing(s) will you do tomorrow to overcome the lies and live more fully in the truth, no matter the cost?

_____

_____

4. **A Daily Record of the Truth:** What thoughts, truths, or observations do you want to record today so that they cannot be erased or forgotten?

_____

_____

_____

_____

_____

_____

Day 170

1. **Gratitude Exercise:** What is one extraordinarily beautiful truth about the world that you noticed today?

_____

_____

_____

2. **Examine Your Actions:** Where have you been challenged today? Where have you compromised the truth or fail to live up to the fullness of justice? What are your struggles and challenges living for the sake of Truth?

_____

_____

_____

3. **Resolution for living in Truth & Freedom:** What concrete thing(s) will you do tomorrow to overcome the lies and live more fully in the truth, no matter the cost?

_____

_____

4. **A Daily Record of the Truth:** What thoughts, truths, or observations do you want to record today so that they cannot be erased or forgotten?

_____

_____

_____

_____

_____

_____

Day 171

1. **Gratitude Exercise:** What is one extraordinarily beautiful truth about the world that you noticed today?

_____

_____

_____

2. **Examine Your Actions:** Where have you been challenged today? Where have you compromised the truth or fail to live up to the fullness of justice? What are your struggles and challenges living for the sake of Truth?

_____

_____

_____

3. **Resolution for living in Truth & Freedom:** What concrete thing(s) will you do tomorrow to overcome the lies and live more fully in the truth, no matter the cost?

_____

_____

4. **A Daily Record of the Truth:** What thoughts, truths, or observations do you want to record today so that they cannot be erased or forgotten?

_____

_____

_____

_____

_____

_____

Day 172

1. **Gratitude Exercise:** What is one extraordinarily beautiful truth about the world that you noticed today?

   _____

   _____

   _____

2. **Examine Your Actions:** Where have you been challenged today? Where have you compromised the truth or fail to live up to the fullness of justice? What are your struggles and challenges living for the sake of Truth?

   _____

   _____

   _____

3. **Resolution for living in Truth & Freedom:** What concrete thing(s) will you do tomorrow to overcome the lies and live more fully in the truth, no matter the cost?

   _____

   _____

4. **A Daily Record of the Truth:** What thoughts, truths, or observations do you want to record today so that they cannot be erased or forgotten?

   _____

   _____

   _____

   _____

   _____

Day 173

1. **Gratitude Exercise:** What is one extraordinarily beautiful truth about the world that you noticed today?

_____

_____

_____

2. **Examine Your Actions:** Where have you been challenged today? Where have you compromised the truth or fail to live up to the fullness of justice? What are your struggles and challenges living for the sake of Truth?

_____

_____

_____

3. **Resolution for living in Truth & Freedom:** What concrete thing(s) will you do tomorrow to overcome the lies and live more fully in the truth, no matter the cost?

_____

_____

4. **A Daily Record of the Truth:** What thoughts, truths, or observations do you want to record today so that they cannot be erased or forgotten?

_____

_____

_____

_____

_____

Day 174

1. **Gratitude Exercise:** What is one extraordinarily beautiful truth about the world that you noticed today?

_____

_____

_____

2. **Examine Your Actions:** Where have you been challenged today? Where have you compromised the truth or fail to live up to the fullness of justice? What are your struggles and challenges living for the sake of Truth?

_____

_____

_____

3. **Resolution for living in Truth & Freedom:** What concrete thing(s) will you do tomorrow to overcome the lies and live more fully in the truth, no matter the cost?

_____

_____

4. **A Daily Record of the Truth:** What thoughts, truths, or observations do you want to record today so that they cannot be erased or forgotten?

_____

_____

_____

_____

_____

_____

Day 175

1. **Gratitude Exercise:** What is one extraordinarily beautiful truth about the world that you noticed today?

_____

_____

_____

2. **Examine Your Actions:** Where have you been challenged today? Where have you compromised the truth or fail to live up to the fullness of justice? What are your struggles and challenges living for the sake of Truth?

_____

_____

_____

3. **Resolution for living in Truth & Freedom:** What concrete thing(s) will you do tomorrow to overcome the lies and live more fully in the truth, no matter the cost?

_____

_____

4. **A Daily Record of the Truth:** What thoughts, truths, or observations do you want to record today so that they cannot be erased or forgotten?

_____

_____

_____

_____

_____

Day 176

1. **Gratitude Exercise:** What is one extraordinarily beautiful truth about the world that you noticed today?

_____

_____

_____

2. **Examine Your Actions:** Where have you been challenged today? Where have you compromised the truth or fail to live up to the fullness of justice? What are your struggles and challenges living for the sake of Truth?

_____

_____

_____

3. **Resolution for living in Truth & Freedom:** What concrete thing(s) will you do tomorrow to overcome the lies and live more fully in the truth, no matter the cost?

_____

_____

4. **A Daily Record of the Truth:** What thoughts, truths, or observations do you want to record today so that they cannot be erased or forgotten?

_____

_____

_____

_____

_____

_____

Day 177

1. **Gratitude Exercise:** What is one extraordinarily beautiful truth about the world that you noticed today?

_____

_____

_____

2. **Examine Your Actions:** Where have you been challenged today? Where have you compromised the truth or fail to live up to the fullness of justice? What are your struggles and challenges living for the sake of Truth?

_____

_____

_____

3. **Resolution for living in Truth & Freedom:** What concrete thing(s) will you do tomorrow to overcome the lies and live more fully in the truth, no matter the cost?

_____

_____

4. **A Daily Record of the Truth:** What thoughts, truths, or observations do you want to record today so that they cannot be erased or forgotten?

_____

_____

_____

_____

_____

_____

Day 178

1. **Gratitude Exercise:** What is one extraordinarily beautiful truth about the world that you noticed today?

_____

_____

_____

2. **Examine Your Actions:** Where have you been challenged today? Where have you compromised the truth or fail to live up to the fullness of justice? What are your struggles and challenges living for the sake of Truth?

_____

_____

_____

3. **Resolution for living in Truth & Freedom:** What concrete thing(s) will you do tomorrow to overcome the lies and live more fully in the truth, no matter the cost?

_____

_____

4. **A Daily Record of the Truth:** What thoughts, truths, or observations do you want to record today so that they cannot be erased or forgotten?

_____

_____

_____

_____

_____

_____

Day 179

1. **Gratitude Exercise:** What is one extraordinarily beautiful truth about the world that you noticed today?

_____

_____

_____

2. **Examine Your Actions:** Where have you been challenged today? Where have you compromised the truth or fail to live up to the fullness of justice? What are your struggles and challenges living for the sake of Truth?

_____

_____

_____

3. **Resolution for living in Truth & Freedom:** What concrete thing(s) will you do tomorrow to overcome the lies and live more fully in the truth, no matter the cost?

_____

_____

4. **A Daily Record of the Truth:** What thoughts, truths, or observations do you want to record today so that they cannot be erased or forgotten?

_____

_____

_____

_____

_____

_____

Day 180

1. **Gratitude Exercise:** What is one extraordinarily beautiful truth about the world that you noticed today?

_____

_____

_____

2. **Examine Your Actions:** Where have you been challenged today? Where have you compromised the truth or fail to live up to the fullness of justice? What are your struggles and challenges living for the sake of Truth?

_____

_____

_____

3. **Resolution for living in Truth & Freedom:** What concrete thing(s) will you do tomorrow to overcome the lies and live more fully in the truth, no matter the cost?

_____

_____

4. **A Daily Record of the Truth:** What thoughts, truths, or observations do you want to record today so that they cannot be erased or forgotten?

_____

_____

_____

_____

_____

_____

Day 181

1. **Gratitude Exercise:** What is one extraordinarily beautiful truth about the world that you noticed today?

    _____

    _____

    _____

2. **Examine Your Actions:** Where have you been challenged today? Where have you compromised the truth or fail to live up to the fullness of justice? What are your struggles and challenges living for the sake of Truth?

    _____

    _____

    _____

3. **Resolution for living in Truth & Freedom:** What concrete thing(s) will you do tomorrow to overcome the lies and live more fully in the truth, no matter the cost?

    _____

    _____

4. **A Daily Record of the Truth:** What thoughts, truths, or observations do you want to record today so that they cannot be erased or forgotten?

    _____

    _____

    _____

    _____

    _____

Day 182

1. **Gratitude Exercise:** What is one extraordinarily beautiful truth about the world that you noticed today?

    _____

    _____

    _____

2. **Examine Your Actions:** Where have you been challenged today? Where have you compromised the truth or fail to live up to the fullness of justice? What are your struggles and challenges living for the sake of Truth?

    _____

    _____

    _____

3. **Resolution for living in Truth & Freedom:** What concrete thing(s) will you do tomorrow to overcome the lies and live more fully in the truth, no matter the cost?

    _____

    _____

4. **A Daily Record of the Truth:** What thoughts, truths, or observations do you want to record today so that they cannot be erased or forgotten?

    _____

    _____

    _____

    _____

    _____

    _____

Day 183

1. **Gratitude Exercise:** What is one extraordinarily beautiful truth about the world that you noticed today?

_____

_____

_____

2. **Examine Your Actions:** Where have you been challenged today? Where have you compromised the truth or fail to live up to the fullness of justice? What are your struggles and challenges living for the sake of Truth?

_____

_____

_____

3. **Resolution for living in Truth & Freedom:** What concrete thing(s) will you do tomorrow to overcome the lies and live more fully in the truth, no matter the cost?

_____

_____

4. **A Daily Record of the Truth:** What thoughts, truths, or observations do you want to record today so that they cannot be erased or forgotten?

_____

_____

_____

_____

_____

_____

Day 184

1. **Gratitude Exercise:** What is one extraordinarily beautiful truth about the world that you noticed today?

   _____

   _____

   _____

2. **Examine Your Actions:** Where have you been challenged today? Where have you compromised the truth or fail to live up to the fullness of justice? What are your struggles and challenges living for the sake of Truth?

   _____

   _____

   _____

3. **Resolution for living in Truth & Freedom:** What concrete thing(s) will you do tomorrow to overcome the lies and live more fully in the truth, no matter the cost?

   _____

   _____

4. **A Daily Record of the Truth:** What thoughts, truths, or observations do you want to record today so that they cannot be erased or forgotten?

   _____

   _____

   _____

   _____

   _____

   _____

Day 185

1. **Gratitude Exercise:** What is one extraordinarily beautiful truth about the world that you noticed today?

_____

_____

_____

2. **Examine Your Actions:** Where have you been challenged today? Where have you compromised the truth or fail to live up to the fullness of justice? What are your struggles and challenges living for the sake of Truth?

_____

_____

_____

3. **Resolution for living in Truth & Freedom:** What concrete thing(s) will you do tomorrow to overcome the lies and live more fully in the truth, no matter the cost?

_____

_____

4. **A Daily Record of the Truth:** What thoughts, truths, or observations do you want to record today so that they cannot be erased or forgotten?

_____

_____

_____

_____

_____

_____

Day 186

1. **Gratitude Exercise:** What is one extraordinarily beautiful truth about the world that you noticed today?

_____

_____

_____

2. **Examine Your Actions:** Where have you been challenged today? Where have you compromised the truth or fail to live up to the fullness of justice? What are your struggles and challenges living for the sake of Truth?

_____

_____

_____

3. **Resolution for living in Truth & Freedom:** What concrete thing(s) will you do tomorrow to overcome the lies and live more fully in the truth, no matter the cost?

_____

_____

4. **A Daily Record of the Truth:** What thoughts, truths, or observations do you want to record today so that they cannot be erased or forgotten?

_____

_____

_____

_____

_____

Day 187

1. **Gratitude Exercise:** What is one extraordinarily beautiful truth about the world that you noticed today?

_____

_____

_____

2. **Examine Your Actions:** Where have you been challenged today? Where have you compromised the truth or fail to live up to the fullness of justice? What are your struggles and challenges living for the sake of Truth?

_____

_____

_____

3. **Resolution for living in Truth & Freedom:** What concrete thing(s) will you do tomorrow to overcome the lies and live more fully in the truth, no matter the cost?

_____

_____

4. **A Daily Record of the Truth:** What thoughts, truths, or observations do you want to record today so that they cannot be erased or forgotten?

_____

_____

_____

_____

_____

_____

Day 188

1. **Gratitude Exercise:** What is one extraordinarily beautiful truth about the world that you noticed today?

    _____

    _____

    _____

2. **Examine Your Actions:** Where have you been challenged today? Where have you compromised the truth or fail to live up to the fullness of justice? What are your struggles and challenges living for the sake of Truth?

    _____

    _____

    _____

3. **Resolution for living in Truth & Freedom:** What concrete thing(s) will you do tomorrow to overcome the lies and live more fully in the truth, no matter the cost?

    _____

    _____

4. **A Daily Record of the Truth:** What thoughts, truths, or observations do you want to record today so that they cannot be erased or forgotten?

    _____

    _____

    _____

    _____

    _____

Day 189

1. **Gratitude Exercise:** What is one extraordinarily beautiful truth about the world that you noticed today?

_____

_____

_____

2. **Examine Your Actions:** Where have you been challenged today? Where have you compromised the truth or fail to live up to the fullness of justice? What are your struggles and challenges living for the sake of Truth?

_____

_____

_____

3. **Resolution for living in Truth & Freedom:** What concrete thing(s) will you do tomorrow to overcome the lies and live more fully in the truth, no matter the cost?

_____

_____

4. **A Daily Record of the Truth:** What thoughts, truths, or observations do you want to record today so that they cannot be erased or forgotten?

_____

_____

_____

_____

_____

_____

Day 190

1. **Gratitude Exercise:** What is one extraordinarily beautiful truth about the world that you noticed today?

_____

_____

_____

2. **Examine Your Actions:** Where have you been challenged today? Where have you compromised the truth or fail to live up to the fullness of justice? What are your struggles and challenges living for the sake of Truth?

_____

_____

_____

3. **Resolution for living in Truth & Freedom:** What concrete thing(s) will you do tomorrow to overcome the lies and live more fully in the truth, no matter the cost?

_____

_____

4. **A Daily Record of the Truth:** What thoughts, truths, or observations do you want to record today so that they cannot be erased or forgotten?

_____

_____

_____

_____

_____

_____

Day 191

1. **Gratitude Exercise:** What is one extraordinarily beautiful truth about the world that you noticed today?

_____

_____

_____

2. **Examine Your Actions:** Where have you been challenged today? Where have you compromised the truth or fail to live up to the fullness of justice? What are your struggles and challenges living for the sake of Truth?

_____

_____

_____

3. **Resolution for living in Truth & Freedom:** What concrete thing(s) will you do tomorrow to overcome the lies and live more fully in the truth, no matter the cost?

_____

_____

4. **A Daily Record of the Truth:** What thoughts, truths, or observations do you want to record today so that they cannot be erased or forgotten?

_____

_____

_____

_____

_____

Day 192

1. **Gratitude Exercise:** What is one extraordinarily beautiful truth about the world that you noticed today?

    _____

    _____

    _____

2. **Examine Your Actions:** Where have you been challenged today? Where have you compromised the truth or fail to live up to the fullness of justice? What are your struggles and challenges living for the sake of Truth?

    _____

    _____

    _____

3. **Resolution for living in Truth & Freedom:** What concrete thing(s) will you do tomorrow to overcome the lies and live more fully in the truth, no matter the cost?

    _____

    _____

4. **A Daily Record of the Truth:** What thoughts, truths, or observations do you want to record today so that they cannot be erased or forgotten?

    _____

    _____

    _____

    _____

    _____

    _____

Day 193

1. **Gratitude Exercise:** What is one extraordinarily beautiful truth about the world that you noticed today?

_____

_____

_____

2. **Examine Your Actions:** Where have you been challenged today? Where have you compromised the truth or fail to live up to the fullness of justice? What are your struggles and challenges living for the sake of Truth?

_____

_____

_____

3. **Resolution for living in Truth & Freedom:** What concrete thing(s) will you do tomorrow to overcome the lies and live more fully in the truth, no matter the cost?

_____

_____

4. **A Daily Record of the Truth:** What thoughts, truths, or observations do you want to record today so that they cannot be erased or forgotten?

_____

_____

_____

_____

_____

_____

Day 194

1. **Gratitude Exercise:** What is one extraordinarily beautiful truth about the world that you noticed today?

_____

_____

_____

2. **Examine Your Actions:** Where have you been challenged today? Where have you compromised the truth or fail to live up to the fullness of justice? What are your struggles and challenges living for the sake of Truth?

_____

_____

_____

3. **Resolution for living in Truth & Freedom:** What concrete thing(s) will you do tomorrow to overcome the lies and live more fully in the truth, no matter the cost?

_____

_____

4. **A Daily Record of the Truth:** What thoughts, truths, or observations do you want to record today so that they cannot be erased or forgotten?

_____

_____

_____

_____

_____

_____

Day 195

1. **Gratitude Exercise:** What is one extraordinarily beautiful truth about the world that you noticed today?

_____

_____

_____

2. **Examine Your Actions:** Where have you been challenged today? Where have you compromised the truth or fail to live up to the fullness of justice? What are your struggles and challenges living for the sake of Truth?

_____

_____

_____

3. **Resolution for living in Truth & Freedom:** What concrete thing(s) will you do tomorrow to overcome the lies and live more fully in the truth, no matter the cost?

_____

_____

4. **A Daily Record of the Truth:** What thoughts, truths, or observations do you want to record today so that they cannot be erased or forgotten?

_____

_____

_____

_____

_____

_____

Day 196

1. **Gratitude Exercise:** What is one extraordinarily beautiful truth about the world that you noticed today?

_____

_____

_____

2. **Examine Your Actions:** Where have you been challenged today? Where have you compromised the truth or fail to live up to the fullness of justice? What are your struggles and challenges living for the sake of Truth?

_____

_____

_____

3. **Resolution for living in Truth & Freedom:** What concrete thing(s) will you do tomorrow to overcome the lies and live more fully in the truth, no matter the cost?

_____

_____

4. **A Daily Record of the Truth:** What thoughts, truths, or observations do you want to record today so that they cannot be erased or forgotten?

_____

_____

_____

_____

_____

_____

Day 197

1. **Gratitude Exercise:** What is one extraordinarily beautiful truth about the world that you noticed today?

_____

_____

_____

2. **Examine Your Actions:** Where have you been challenged today? Where have you compromised the truth or fail to live up to the fullness of justice? What are your struggles and challenges living for the sake of Truth?

_____

_____

_____

3. **Resolution for living in Truth & Freedom:** What concrete thing(s) will you do tomorrow to overcome the lies and live more fully in the truth, no matter the cost?

_____

_____

4. **A Daily Record of the Truth:** What thoughts, truths, or observations do you want to record today so that they cannot be erased or forgotten?

_____

_____

_____

_____

_____

_____

Day 198

1. **Gratitude Exercise:** What is one extraordinarily beautiful truth about the world that you noticed today?

_____

_____

_____

2. **Examine Your Actions:** Where have you been challenged today? Where have you compromised the truth or fail to live up to the fullness of justice? What are your struggles and challenges living for the sake of Truth?

_____

_____

_____

3. **Resolution for living in Truth & Freedom:** What concrete thing(s) will you do tomorrow to overcome the lies and live more fully in the truth, no matter the cost?

_____

_____

4. **A Daily Record of the Truth:** What thoughts, truths, or observations do you want to record today so that they cannot be erased or forgotten?

_____

_____

_____

_____

_____

_____

Day 199

1. **Gratitude Exercise:** What is one extraordinarily beautiful truth about the world that you noticed today?

_____

_____

_____

2. **Examine Your Actions:** Where have you been challenged today? Where have you compromised the truth or fail to live up to the fullness of justice? What are your struggles and challenges living for the sake of Truth?

_____

_____

_____

3. **Resolution for living in Truth & Freedom:** What concrete thing(s) will you do tomorrow to overcome the lies and live more fully in the truth, no matter the cost?

_____

_____

4. **A Daily Record of the Truth:** What thoughts, truths, or observations do you want to record today so that they cannot be erased or forgotten?

_____

_____

_____

_____

_____

_____

Day 200

1. **Gratitude Exercise:** What is one extraordinarily beautiful truth about the world that you noticed today?

_____

_____

_____

2. **Examine Your Actions:** Where have you been challenged today? Where have you compromised the truth or fail to live up to the fullness of justice? What are your struggles and challenges living for the sake of Truth?

_____

_____

_____

3. **Resolution for living in Truth & Freedom:** What concrete thing(s) will you do tomorrow to overcome the lies and live more fully in the truth, no matter the cost?

_____

_____

4. **A Daily Record of the Truth:** What thoughts, truths, or observations do you want to record today so that they cannot be erased or forgotten?

_____

_____

_____

_____

_____

_____

Day 201

1. **Gratitude Exercise:** What is one extraordinarily beautiful truth about the world that you noticed today?

_____

_____

_____

2. **Examine Your Actions:** Where have you been challenged today? Where have you compromised the truth or fail to live up to the fullness of justice? What are your struggles and challenges living for the sake of Truth?

_____

_____

_____

3. **Resolution for living in Truth & Freedom:** What concrete thing(s) will you do tomorrow to overcome the lies and live more fully in the truth, no matter the cost?

_____

_____

4. **A Daily Record of the Truth:** What thoughts, truths, or observations do you want to record today so that they cannot be erased or forgotten?

_____

_____

_____

_____

_____

_____

Day 202

1. **Gratitude Exercise:** What is one extraordinarily beautiful truth about the world that you noticed today?

_____

_____

_____

2. **Examine Your Actions:** Where have you been challenged today? Where have you compromised the truth or fail to live up to the fullness of justice? What are your struggles and challenges living for the sake of Truth?

_____

_____

_____

3. **Resolution for living in Truth & Freedom:** What concrete thing(s) will you do tomorrow to overcome the lies and live more fully in the truth, no matter the cost?

_____

_____

4. **A Daily Record of the Truth:** What thoughts, truths, or observations do you want to record today so that they cannot be erased or forgotten?

_____

_____

_____

_____

_____

_____

Day 203

1. **Gratitude Exercise:** What is one extraordinarily beautiful truth about the world that you noticed today?

_____

_____

_____

2. **Examine Your Actions:** Where have you been challenged today? Where have you compromised the truth or fail to live up to the fullness of justice? What are your struggles and challenges living for the sake of Truth?

_____

_____

_____

3. **Resolution for living in Truth & Freedom:** What concrete thing(s) will you do tomorrow to overcome the lies and live more fully in the truth, no matter the cost?

_____

_____

4. **A Daily Record of the Truth:** What thoughts, truths, or observations do you want to record today so that they cannot be erased or forgotten?

_____

_____

_____

_____

_____

Day 204

1. **Gratitude Exercise:** What is one extraordinarily beautiful truth about the world that you noticed today?

_____

_____

_____

2. **Examine Your Actions:** Where have you been challenged today? Where have you compromised the truth or fail to live up to the fullness of justice? What are your struggles and challenges living for the sake of Truth?

_____

_____

_____

3. **Resolution for living in Truth & Freedom:** What concrete thing(s) will you do tomorrow to overcome the lies and live more fully in the truth, no matter the cost?

_____

_____

4. **A Daily Record of the Truth:** What thoughts, truths, or observations do you want to record today so that they cannot be erased or forgotten?

_____

_____

_____

_____

_____

_____

Day 205

1. **Gratitude Exercise:** What is one extraordinarily beautiful truth about the world that you noticed today?

_____

_____

_____

2. **Examine Your Actions:** Where have you been challenged today? Where have you compromised the truth or fail to live up to the fullness of justice? What are your struggles and challenges living for the sake of Truth?

_____

_____

_____

3. **Resolution for living in Truth & Freedom:** What concrete thing(s) will you do tomorrow to overcome the lies and live more fully in the truth, no matter the cost?

_____

_____

4. **A Daily Record of the Truth:** What thoughts, truths, or observations do you want to record today so that they cannot be erased or forgotten?

_____

_____

_____

_____

_____

_____

Day 206

1. **Gratitude Exercise:** What is one extraordinarily beautiful truth about the world that you noticed today?

_____

_____

_____

2. **Examine Your Actions:** Where have you been challenged today? Where have you compromised the truth or fail to live up to the fullness of justice? What are your struggles and challenges living for the sake of Truth?

_____

_____

_____

3. **Resolution for living in Truth & Freedom:** What concrete thing(s) will you do tomorrow to overcome the lies and live more fully in the truth, no matter the cost?

_____

_____

4. **A Daily Record of the Truth:** What thoughts, truths, or observations do you want to record today so that they cannot be erased or forgotten?

_____

_____

_____

_____

_____

_____

Day 207

1. **Gratitude Exercise:** What is one extraordinarily beautiful truth about the world that you noticed today?

_____

_____

_____

2. **Examine Your Actions:** Where have you been challenged today? Where have you compromised the truth or fail to live up to the fullness of justice? What are your struggles and challenges living for the sake of Truth?

_____

_____

_____

3. **Resolution for living in Truth & Freedom:** What concrete thing(s) will you do tomorrow to overcome the lies and live more fully in the truth, no matter the cost?

_____

_____

4. **A Daily Record of the Truth:** What thoughts, truths, or observations do you want to record today so that they cannot be erased or forgotten?

_____

_____

_____

_____

_____

_____

Day 208

1. **Gratitude Exercise:** What is one extraordinarily beautiful truth about the world that you noticed today?

_____

_____

_____

2. **Examine Your Actions:** Where have you been challenged today? Where have you compromised the truth or fail to live up to the fullness of justice? What are your struggles and challenges living for the sake of Truth?

_____

_____

_____

3. **Resolution for living in Truth & Freedom:** What concrete thing(s) will you do tomorrow to overcome the lies and live more fully in the truth, no matter the cost?

_____

_____

4. **A Daily Record of the Truth:** What thoughts, truths, or observations do you want to record today so that they cannot be erased or forgotten?

_____

_____

_____

_____

_____

_____

Day 209

1. **Gratitude Exercise:** What is one extraordinarily beautiful truth about the world that you noticed today?

   _____

   _____

   _____

2. **Examine Your Actions:** Where have you been challenged today? Where have you compromised the truth or fail to live up to the fullness of justice? What are your struggles and challenges living for the sake of Truth?

   _____

   _____

   _____

3. **Resolution for living in Truth & Freedom:** What concrete thing(s) will you do tomorrow to overcome the lies and live more fully in the truth, no matter the cost?

   _____

   _____

4. **A Daily Record of the Truth:** What thoughts, truths, or observations do you want to record today so that they cannot be erased or forgotten?

   _____

   _____

   _____

   _____

   _____

   _____

Day 210

1. **Gratitude Exercise:** What is one extraordinarily beautiful truth about the world that you noticed today?

_____

_____

_____

2. **Examine Your Actions:** Where have you been challenged today? Where have you compromised the truth or fail to live up to the fullness of justice? What are your struggles and challenges living for the sake of Truth?

_____

_____

_____

3. **Resolution for living in Truth & Freedom:** What concrete thing(s) will you do tomorrow to overcome the lies and live more fully in the truth, no matter the cost?

_____

_____

4. **A Daily Record of the Truth:** What thoughts, truths, or observations do you want to record today so that they cannot be erased or forgotten?

_____

_____

_____

_____

_____

_____

Day 211

1. **Gratitude Exercise:** What is one extraordinarily beautiful truth about the world that you noticed today?

_____

_____

_____

2. **Examine Your Actions:** Where have you been challenged today? Where have you compromised the truth or fail to live up to the fullness of justice? What are your struggles and challenges living for the sake of Truth?

_____

_____

_____

3. **Resolution for living in Truth & Freedom:** What concrete thing(s) will you do tomorrow to overcome the lies and live more fully in the truth, no matter the cost?

_____

_____

4. **A Daily Record of the Truth:** What thoughts, truths, or observations do you want to record today so that they cannot be erased or forgotten?

_____

_____

_____

_____

_____

_____

Day 212

1. **Gratitude Exercise:** What is one extraordinarily beautiful truth about the world that you noticed today?

_____

_____

_____

2. **Examine Your Actions:** Where have you been challenged today? Where have you compromised the truth or fail to live up to the fullness of justice? What are your struggles and challenges living for the sake of Truth?

_____

_____

_____

3. **Resolution for living in Truth & Freedom:** What concrete thing(s) will you do tomorrow to overcome the lies and live more fully in the truth, no matter the cost?

_____

_____

4. **A Daily Record of the Truth:** What thoughts, truths, or observations do you want to record today so that they cannot be erased or forgotten?

_____

_____

_____

_____

_____

_____

Day 213

1. **Gratitude Exercise:** What is one extraordinarily beautiful truth about the world that you noticed today?

_____

_____

_____

2. **Examine Your Actions:** Where have you been challenged today? Where have you compromised the truth or fail to live up to the fullness of justice? What are your struggles and challenges living for the sake of Truth?

_____

_____

_____

3. **Resolution for living in Truth & Freedom:** What concrete thing(s) will you do tomorrow to overcome the lies and live more fully in the truth, no matter the cost?

_____

_____

4. **A Daily Record of the Truth:** What thoughts, truths, or observations do you want to record today so that they cannot be erased or forgotten?

_____

_____

_____

_____

_____

_____

Day 214

1. **Gratitude Exercise:** What is one extraordinarily beautiful truth about the world that you noticed today?

_____

_____

_____

2. **Examine Your Actions:** Where have you been challenged today? Where have you compromised the truth or fail to live up to the fullness of justice? What are your struggles and challenges living for the sake of Truth?

_____

_____

_____

3. **Resolution for living in Truth & Freedom:** What concrete thing(s) will you do tomorrow to overcome the lies and live more fully in the truth, no matter the cost?

_____

_____

4. **A Daily Record of the Truth:** What thoughts, truths, or observations do you want to record today so that they cannot be erased or forgotten?

_____

_____

_____

_____

_____

Day 215

1. **Gratitude Exercise:** What is one extraordinarily beautiful truth about the world that you noticed today?

_____

_____

_____

2. **Examine Your Actions:** Where have you been challenged today? Where have you compromised the truth or fail to live up to the fullness of justice? What are your struggles and challenges living for the sake of Truth?

_____

_____

_____

3. **Resolution for living in Truth & Freedom:** What concrete thing(s) will you do tomorrow to overcome the lies and live more fully in the truth, no matter the cost?

_____

_____

4. **A Daily Record of the Truth:** What thoughts, truths, or observations do you want to record today so that they cannot be erased or forgotten?

_____

_____

_____

_____

_____

Day 216

1. **Gratitude Exercise:** What is one extraordinarily beautiful truth about the world that you noticed today?

    _____

    _____

    _____

2. **Examine Your Actions:** Where have you been challenged today? Where have you compromised the truth or fail to live up to the fullness of justice? What are your struggles and challenges living for the sake of Truth?

    _____

    _____

    _____

3. **Resolution for living in Truth & Freedom:** What concrete thing(s) will you do tomorrow to overcome the lies and live more fully in the truth, no matter the cost?

    _____

    _____

4. **A Daily Record of the Truth:** What thoughts, truths, or observations do you want to record today so that they cannot be erased or forgotten?

    _____

    _____

    _____

    _____

    _____

    _____

Day 217

1. **Gratitude Exercise:** What is one extraordinarily beautiful truth about the world that you noticed today?

_____

_____

_____

2. **Examine Your Actions:** Where have you been challenged today? Where have you compromised the truth or fail to live up to the fullness of justice? What are your struggles and challenges living for the sake of Truth?

_____

_____

_____

3. **Resolution for living in Truth & Freedom:** What concrete thing(s) will you do tomorrow to overcome the lies and live more fully in the truth, no matter the cost?

_____

_____

4. **A Daily Record of the Truth:** What thoughts, truths, or observations do you want to record today so that they cannot be erased or forgotten?

_____

_____

_____

_____

_____

_____

Day 218

1. **Gratitude Exercise:** What is one extraordinarily beautiful truth about the world that you noticed today?

_____

_____

_____

2. **Examine Your Actions:** Where have you been challenged today? Where have you compromised the truth or fail to live up to the fullness of justice? What are your struggles and challenges living for the sake of Truth?

_____

_____

_____

3. **Resolution for living in Truth & Freedom:** What concrete thing(s) will you do tomorrow to overcome the lies and live more fully in the truth, no matter the cost?

_____

_____

4. **A Daily Record of the Truth:** What thoughts, truths, or observations do you want to record today so that they cannot be erased or forgotten?

_____

_____

_____

_____

_____

_____

Day 219

1. **Gratitude Exercise:** What is one extraordinarily beautiful truth about the world that you noticed today?

_____

_____

_____

2. **Examine Your Actions:** Where have you been challenged today? Where have you compromised the truth or fail to live up to the fullness of justice? What are your struggles and challenges living for the sake of Truth?

_____

_____

_____

3. **Resolution for living in Truth & Freedom:** What concrete thing(s) will you do tomorrow to overcome the lies and live more fully in the truth, no matter the cost?

_____

_____

4. **A Daily Record of the Truth:** What thoughts, truths, or observations do you want to record today so that they cannot be erased or forgotten?

_____

_____

_____

_____

_____

Day 220

1. **Gratitude Exercise:** What is one extraordinarily beautiful truth about the world that you noticed today?

    _____

    _____

    _____

2. **Examine Your Actions:** Where have you been challenged today? Where have you compromised the truth or fail to live up to the fullness of justice? What are your struggles and challenges living for the sake of Truth?

    _____

    _____

    _____

3. **Resolution for living in Truth & Freedom:** What concrete thing(s) will you do tomorrow to overcome the lies and live more fully in the truth, no matter the cost?

    _____

    _____

4. **A Daily Record of the Truth:** What thoughts, truths, or observations do you want to record today so that they cannot be erased or forgotten?

    _____

    _____

    _____

    _____

    _____

    _____

Day 221

1. **Gratitude Exercise:** What is one extraordinarily beautiful truth about the world that you noticed today?

_____

_____

_____

2. **Examine Your Actions:** Where have you been challenged today? Where have you compromised the truth or fail to live up to the fullness of justice? What are your struggles and challenges living for the sake of Truth?

_____

_____

_____

3. **Resolution for living in Truth & Freedom:** What concrete thing(s) will you do tomorrow to overcome the lies and live more fully in the truth, no matter the cost?

_____

_____

4. **A Daily Record of the Truth:** What thoughts, truths, or observations do you want to record today so that they cannot be erased or forgotten?

_____

_____

_____

_____

_____

_____

Day 222

1. **Gratitude Exercise:** What is one extraordinarily beautiful truth about the world that you noticed today?

_____

_____

_____

2. **Examine Your Actions:** Where have you been challenged today? Where have you compromised the truth or fail to live up to the fullness of justice? What are your struggles and challenges living for the sake of Truth?

_____

_____

_____

3. **Resolution for living in Truth & Freedom:** What concrete thing(s) will you do tomorrow to overcome the lies and live more fully in the truth, no matter the cost?

_____

_____

4. **A Daily Record of the Truth:** What thoughts, truths, or observations do you want to record today so that they cannot be erased or forgotten?

_____

_____

_____

_____

_____

_____

Day 223

1. **Gratitude Exercise:** What is one extraordinarily beautiful truth about the world that you noticed today?

_____

_____

_____

2. **Examine Your Actions:** Where have you been challenged today? Where have you compromised the truth or fail to live up to the fullness of justice? What are your struggles and challenges living for the sake of Truth?

_____

_____

_____

3. **Resolution for living in Truth & Freedom:** What concrete thing(s) will you do tomorrow to overcome the lies and live more fully in the truth, no matter the cost?

_____

_____

4. **A Daily Record of the Truth:** What thoughts, truths, or observations do you want to record today so that they cannot be erased or forgotten?

_____

_____

_____

_____

_____

Day 224

1. **Gratitude Exercise:** What is one extraordinarily beautiful truth about the world that you noticed today?

_____

_____

_____

2. **Examine Your Actions:** Where have you been challenged today? Where have you compromised the truth or fail to live up to the fullness of justice? What are your struggles and challenges living for the sake of Truth?

_____

_____

_____

3. **Resolution for living in Truth & Freedom:** What concrete thing(s) will you do tomorrow to overcome the lies and live more fully in the truth, no matter the cost?

_____

_____

4. **A Daily Record of the Truth:** What thoughts, truths, or observations do you want to record today so that they cannot be erased or forgotten?

_____

_____

_____

_____

_____

_____

Day 225

1. **Gratitude Exercise:** What is one extraordinarily beautiful truth about the world that you noticed today?

_____

_____

_____

2. **Examine Your Actions:** Where have you been challenged today? Where have you compromised the truth or fail to live up to the fullness of justice? What are your struggles and challenges living for the sake of Truth?

_____

_____

_____

3. **Resolution for living in Truth & Freedom:** What concrete thing(s) will you do tomorrow to overcome the lies and live more fully in the truth, no matter the cost?

_____

_____

4. **A Daily Record of the Truth:** What thoughts, truths, or observations do you want to record today so that they cannot be erased or forgotten?

_____

_____

_____

_____

_____

Day 226

1. **Gratitude Exercise:** What is one extraordinarily beautiful truth about the world that you noticed today?

_____

_____

_____

2. **Examine Your Actions:** Where have you been challenged today? Where have you compromised the truth or fail to live up to the fullness of justice? What are your struggles and challenges living for the sake of Truth?

_____

_____

_____

3. **Resolution for living in Truth & Freedom:** What concrete thing(s) will you do tomorrow to overcome the lies and live more fully in the truth, no matter the cost?

_____

_____

4. **A Daily Record of the Truth:** What thoughts, truths, or observations do you want to record today so that they cannot be erased or forgotten?

_____

_____

_____

_____

_____

_____

Day 227

1. **Gratitude Exercise:** What is one extraordinarily beautiful truth about the world that you noticed today?

_____

_____

_____

2. **Examine Your Actions:** Where have you been challenged today? Where have you compromised the truth or fail to live up to the fullness of justice? What are your struggles and challenges living for the sake of Truth?

_____

_____

_____

3. **Resolution for living in Truth & Freedom:** What concrete thing(s) will you do tomorrow to overcome the lies and live more fully in the truth, no matter the cost?

_____

_____

4. **A Daily Record of the Truth:** What thoughts, truths, or observations do you want to record today so that they cannot be erased or forgotten?

_____

_____

_____

_____

_____

_____

Day 228

1. **Gratitude Exercise:** What is one extraordinarily beautiful truth about the world that you noticed today?

_____

_____

_____

2. **Examine Your Actions:** Where have you been challenged today? Where have you compromised the truth or fail to live up to the fullness of justice? What are your struggles and challenges living for the sake of Truth?

_____

_____

_____

3. **Resolution for living in Truth & Freedom:** What concrete thing(s) will you do tomorrow to overcome the lies and live more fully in the truth, no matter the cost?

_____

_____

4. **A Daily Record of the Truth:** What thoughts, truths, or observations do you want to record today so that they cannot be erased or forgotten?

_____

_____

_____

_____

_____

_____

Day 229

1. **Gratitude Exercise:** What is one extraordinarily beautiful truth about the world that you noticed today?

_____

_____

_____

2. **Examine Your Actions:** Where have you been challenged today? Where have you compromised the truth or fail to live up to the fullness of justice? What are your struggles and challenges living for the sake of Truth?

_____

_____

_____

3. **Resolution for living in Truth & Freedom:** What concrete thing(s) will you do tomorrow to overcome the lies and live more fully in the truth, no matter the cost?

_____

_____

4. **A Daily Record of the Truth:** What thoughts, truths, or observations do you want to record today so that they cannot be erased or forgotten?

_____

_____

_____

_____

_____

_____

Day 230

1. **Gratitude Exercise:** What is one extraordinarily beautiful truth about the world that you noticed today?

_____

_____

_____

2. **Examine Your Actions:** Where have you been challenged today? Where have you compromised the truth or fail to live up to the fullness of justice? What are your struggles and challenges living for the sake of Truth?

_____

_____

_____

3. **Resolution for living in Truth & Freedom:** What concrete thing(s) will you do tomorrow to overcome the lies and live more fully in the truth, no matter the cost?

_____

_____

4. **A Daily Record of the Truth:** What thoughts, truths, or observations do you want to record today so that they cannot be erased or forgotten?

_____

_____

_____

_____

_____

_____

Day 231

1. **Gratitude Exercise:** What is one extraordinarily beautiful truth about the world that you noticed today?

_____

_____

_____

2. **Examine Your Actions:** Where have you been challenged today? Where have you compromised the truth or fail to live up to the fullness of justice? What are your struggles and challenges living for the sake of Truth?

_____

_____

_____

3. **Resolution for living in Truth & Freedom:** What concrete thing(s) will you do tomorrow to overcome the lies and live more fully in the truth, no matter the cost?

_____

_____

4. **A Daily Record of the Truth:** What thoughts, truths, or observations do you want to record today so that they cannot be erased or forgotten?

_____

_____

_____

_____

_____

_____

Day 232

1. **Gratitude Exercise:** What is one extraordinarily beautiful truth about the world that you noticed today?

_____

_____

_____

2. **Examine Your Actions:** Where have you been challenged today? Where have you compromised the truth or fail to live up to the fullness of justice? What are your struggles and challenges living for the sake of Truth?

_____

_____

_____

3. **Resolution for living in Truth & Freedom:** What concrete thing(s) will you do tomorrow to overcome the lies and live more fully in the truth, no matter the cost?

_____

_____

4. **A Daily Record of the Truth:** What thoughts, truths, or observations do you want to record today so that they cannot be erased or forgotten?

_____

_____

_____

_____

_____

_____

Day 233

1. **Gratitude Exercise:** What is one extraordinarily beautiful truth about the world that you noticed today?

_____

_____

_____

2. **Examine Your Actions:** Where have you been challenged today? Where have you compromised the truth or fail to live up to the fullness of justice? What are your struggles and challenges living for the sake of Truth?

_____

_____

_____

3. **Resolution for living in Truth & Freedom:** What concrete thing(s) will you do tomorrow to overcome the lies and live more fully in the truth, no matter the cost?

_____

_____

4. **A Daily Record of the Truth:** What thoughts, truths, or observations do you want to record today so that they cannot be erased or forgotten?

_____

_____

_____

_____

_____

Day 234

1. **Gratitude Exercise:** What is one extraordinarily beautiful truth about the world that you noticed today?

   _____

   _____

   _____

2. **Examine Your Actions:** Where have you been challenged today? Where have you compromised the truth or fail to live up to the fullness of justice? What are your struggles and challenges living for the sake of Truth?

   _____

   _____

   _____

3. **Resolution for living in Truth & Freedom:** What concrete thing(s) will you do tomorrow to overcome the lies and live more fully in the truth, no matter the cost?

   _____

   _____

4. **A Daily Record of the Truth:** What thoughts, truths, or observations do you want to record today so that they cannot be erased or forgotten?

   _____

   _____

   _____

   _____

   _____

   _____

Day 235

1. **Gratitude Exercise:** What is one extraordinarily beautiful truth about the world that you noticed today?

_____

_____

_____

2. **Examine Your Actions:** Where have you been challenged today? Where have you compromised the truth or fail to live up to the fullness of justice? What are your struggles and challenges living for the sake of Truth?

_____

_____

_____

3. **Resolution for living in Truth & Freedom:** What concrete thing(s) will you do tomorrow to overcome the lies and live more fully in the truth, no matter the cost?

_____

_____

4. **A Daily Record of the Truth:** What thoughts, truths, or observations do you want to record today so that they cannot be erased or forgotten?

_____

_____

_____

_____

_____

Day 236

1. **Gratitude Exercise:** What is one extraordinarily beautiful truth about the world that you noticed today?

2. **Examine Your Actions:** Where have you been challenged today? Where have you compromised the truth or fail to live up to the fullness of justice? What are your struggles and challenges living for the sake of Truth?

3. **Resolution for living in Truth & Freedom:** What concrete thing(s) will you do tomorrow to overcome the lies and live more fully in the truth, no matter the cost?

4. **A Daily Record of the Truth:** What thoughts, truths, or observations do you want to record today so that they cannot be erased or forgotten?

Day 237

1. **Gratitude Exercise:** What is one extraordinarily beautiful truth about the world that you noticed today?

_____

_____

_____

2. **Examine Your Actions:** Where have you been challenged today? Where have you compromised the truth or fail to live up to the fullness of justice? What are your struggles and challenges living for the sake of Truth?

_____

_____

_____

3. **Resolution for living in Truth & Freedom:** What concrete thing(s) will you do tomorrow to overcome the lies and live more fully in the truth, no matter the cost?

_____

_____

4. **A Daily Record of the Truth:** What thoughts, truths, or observations do you want to record today so that they cannot be erased or forgotten?

_____

_____

_____

_____

_____

_____

Day 238

1. **Gratitude Exercise:** What is one extraordinarily beautiful truth about the world that you noticed today?

_____

_____

_____

2. **Examine Your Actions:** Where have you been challenged today? Where have you compromised the truth or fail to live up to the fullness of justice? What are your struggles and challenges living for the sake of Truth?

_____

_____

_____

3. **Resolution for living in Truth & Freedom:** What concrete thing(s) will you do tomorrow to overcome the lies and live more fully in the truth, no matter the cost?

_____

_____

4. **A Daily Record of the Truth:** What thoughts, truths, or observations do you want to record today so that they cannot be erased or forgotten?

_____

_____

_____

_____

_____

_____

Day 239

1. **Gratitude Exercise:** What is one extraordinarily beautiful truth about the world that you noticed today?

_____

_____

_____

2. **Examine Your Actions:** Where have you been challenged today? Where have you compromised the truth or fail to live up to the fullness of justice? What are your struggles and challenges living for the sake of Truth?

_____

_____

_____

3. **Resolution for living in Truth & Freedom:** What concrete thing(s) will you do tomorrow to overcome the lies and live more fully in the truth, no matter the cost?

_____

_____

4. **A Daily Record of the Truth:** What thoughts, truths, or observations do you want to record today so that they cannot be erased or forgotten?

_____

_____

_____

_____

_____

_____

Day 240

1. **Gratitude Exercise:** What is one extraordinarily beautiful truth about the world that you noticed today?

_____

_____

_____

2. **Examine Your Actions:** Where have you been challenged today? Where have you compromised the truth or fail to live up to the fullness of justice? What are your struggles and challenges living for the sake of Truth?

_____

_____

_____

3. **Resolution for living in Truth & Freedom:** What concrete thing(s) will you do tomorrow to overcome the lies and live more fully in the truth, no matter the cost?

_____

_____

4. **A Daily Record of the Truth:** What thoughts, truths, or observations do you want to record today so that they cannot be erased or forgotten?

_____

_____

_____

_____

_____

_____

Day 241

1. **Gratitude Exercise:** What is one extraordinarily beautiful truth about the world that you noticed today?

_____

_____

_____

2. **Examine Your Actions:** Where have you been challenged today? Where have you compromised the truth or fail to live up to the fullness of justice? What are your struggles and challenges living for the sake of Truth?

_____

_____

_____

3. **Resolution for living in Truth & Freedom:** What concrete thing(s) will you do tomorrow to overcome the lies and live more fully in the truth, no matter the cost?

_____

_____

4. **A Daily Record of the Truth:** What thoughts, truths, or observations do you want to record today so that they cannot be erased or forgotten?

_____

_____

_____

_____

_____

Day 242

1. **Gratitude Exercise:** What is one extraordinarily beautiful truth about the world that you noticed today?

    _____

    _____

    _____

2. **Examine Your Actions:** Where have you been challenged today? Where have you compromised the truth or fail to live up to the fullness of justice? What are your struggles and challenges living for the sake of Truth?

    _____

    _____

    _____

3. **Resolution for living in Truth & Freedom:** What concrete thing(s) will you do tomorrow to overcome the lies and live more fully in the truth, no matter the cost?

    _____

    _____

4. **A Daily Record of the Truth:** What thoughts, truths, or observations do you want to record today so that they cannot be erased or forgotten?

    _____

    _____

    _____

    _____

    _____

    _____

Day 243

1. **Gratitude Exercise:** What is one extraordinarily beautiful truth about the world that you noticed today?

_____

_____

_____

2. **Examine Your Actions:** Where have you been challenged today? Where have you compromised the truth or fail to live up to the fullness of justice? What are your struggles and challenges living for the sake of Truth?

_____

_____

_____

3. **Resolution for living in Truth & Freedom:** What concrete thing(s) will you do tomorrow to overcome the lies and live more fully in the truth, no matter the cost?

_____

_____

4. **A Daily Record of the Truth:** What thoughts, truths, or observations do you want to record today so that they cannot be erased or forgotten?

_____

_____

_____

_____

_____

Day 244

1. **Gratitude Exercise:** What is one extraordinarily beautiful truth about the world that you noticed today?

_____

_____

_____

2. **Examine Your Actions:** Where have you been challenged today? Where have you compromised the truth or fail to live up to the fullness of justice? What are your struggles and challenges living for the sake of Truth?

_____

_____

_____

3. **Resolution for living in Truth & Freedom:** What concrete thing(s) will you do tomorrow to overcome the lies and live more fully in the truth, no matter the cost?

_____

_____

4. **A Daily Record of the Truth:** What thoughts, truths, or observations do you want to record today so that they cannot be erased or forgotten?

_____

_____

_____

_____

_____

_____

Day 245

1. **Gratitude Exercise:** What is one extraordinarily beautiful truth about the world that you noticed today?

---

2. **Examine Your Actions:** Where have you been challenged today? Where have you compromised the truth or fail to live up to the fullness of justice? What are your struggles and challenges living for the sake of Truth?

---

3. **Resolution for living in Truth & Freedom:** What concrete thing(s) will you do tomorrow to overcome the lies and live more fully in the truth, no matter the cost?

---

4. **A Daily Record of the Truth:** What thoughts, truths, or observations do you want to record today so that they cannot be erased or forgotten?

Day 246

1. **Gratitude Exercise:** What is one extraordinarily beautiful truth about the world that you noticed today?

    _____

    _____

    _____

2. **Examine Your Actions:** Where have you been challenged today? Where have you compromised the truth or fail to live up to the fullness of justice? What are your struggles and challenges living for the sake of Truth?

    _____

    _____

    _____

3. **Resolution for living in Truth & Freedom:** What concrete thing(s) will you do tomorrow to overcome the lies and live more fully in the truth, no matter the cost?

    _____

    _____

4. **A Daily Record of the Truth:** What thoughts, truths, or observations do you want to record today so that they cannot be erased or forgotten?

    _____

    _____

    _____

    _____

    _____

    _____

Day 247

1. **Gratitude Exercise:** What is one extraordinarily beautiful truth about the world that you noticed today?

_____

_____

_____

2. **Examine Your Actions:** Where have you been challenged today? Where have you compromised the truth or fail to live up to the fullness of justice? What are your struggles and challenges living for the sake of Truth?

_____

_____

_____

3. **Resolution for living in Truth & Freedom:** What concrete thing(s) will you do tomorrow to overcome the lies and live more fully in the truth, no matter the cost?

_____

_____

4. **A Daily Record of the Truth:** What thoughts, truths, or observations do you want to record today so that they cannot be erased or forgotten?

_____

_____

_____

_____

_____

_____

Day 248

1. **Gratitude Exercise:** What is one extraordinarily beautiful truth about the world that you noticed today?

_____

_____

_____

2. **Examine Your Actions:** Where have you been challenged today? Where have you compromised the truth or fail to live up to the fullness of justice? What are your struggles and challenges living for the sake of Truth?

_____

_____

_____

3. **Resolution for living in Truth & Freedom:** What concrete thing(s) will you do tomorrow to overcome the lies and live more fully in the truth, no matter the cost?

_____

_____

4. **A Daily Record of the Truth:** What thoughts, truths, or observations do you want to record today so that they cannot be erased or forgotten?

_____

_____

_____

_____

_____

_____

Day 249

1. **Gratitude Exercise:** What is one extraordinarily beautiful truth about the world that you noticed today?

   _____

   _____

   _____

2. **Examine Your Actions:** Where have you been challenged today? Where have you compromised the truth or fail to live up to the fullness of justice? What are your struggles and challenges living for the sake of Truth?

   _____

   _____

   _____

3. **Resolution for living in Truth & Freedom:** What concrete thing(s) will you do tomorrow to overcome the lies and live more fully in the truth, no matter the cost?

   _____

   _____

4. **A Daily Record of the Truth:** What thoughts, truths, or observations do you want to record today so that they cannot be erased or forgotten?

   _____

   _____

   _____

   _____

   _____

   _____

Day 250

1. **Gratitude Exercise:** What is one extraordinarily beautiful truth about the world that you noticed today?

    _____

    _____

    _____

2. **Examine Your Actions:** Where have you been challenged today? Where have you compromised the truth or fail to live up to the fullness of justice? What are your struggles and challenges living for the sake of Truth?

    _____

    _____

    _____

3. **Resolution for living in Truth & Freedom:** What concrete thing(s) will you do tomorrow to overcome the lies and live more fully in the truth, no matter the cost?

    _____

    _____

4. **A Daily Record of the Truth:** What thoughts, truths, or observations do you want to record today so that they cannot be erased or forgotten?

    _____

    _____

    _____

    _____

    _____

    _____

Day 251

1. **Gratitude Exercise:** What is one extraordinarily beautiful truth about the world that you noticed today?

_____

_____

_____

2. **Examine Your Actions:** Where have you been challenged today? Where have you compromised the truth or fail to live up to the fullness of justice? What are your struggles and challenges living for the sake of Truth?

_____

_____

_____

3. **Resolution for living in Truth & Freedom:** What concrete thing(s) will you do tomorrow to overcome the lies and live more fully in the truth, no matter the cost?

_____

_____

4. **A Daily Record of the Truth:** What thoughts, truths, or observations do you want to record today so that they cannot be erased or forgotten?

_____

_____

_____

_____

_____

_____

Day 252

1. **Gratitude Exercise:** What is one extraordinarily beautiful truth about the world that you noticed today?

_____

_____

_____

2. **Examine Your Actions:** Where have you been challenged today? Where have you compromised the truth or fail to live up to the fullness of justice? What are your struggles and challenges living for the sake of Truth?

_____

_____

_____

3. **Resolution for living in Truth & Freedom:** What concrete thing(s) will you do tomorrow to overcome the lies and live more fully in the truth, no matter the cost?

_____

_____

4. **A Daily Record of the Truth:** What thoughts, truths, or observations do you want to record today so that they cannot be erased or forgotten?

_____

_____

_____

_____

_____

_____

Day 253

1. **Gratitude Exercise:** What is one extraordinarily beautiful truth about the world that you noticed today?

_____

_____

_____

2. **Examine Your Actions:** Where have you been challenged today? Where have you compromised the truth or fail to live up to the fullness of justice? What are your struggles and challenges living for the sake of Truth?

_____

_____

_____

3. **Resolution for living in Truth & Freedom:** What concrete thing(s) will you do tomorrow to overcome the lies and live more fully in the truth, no matter the cost?

_____

_____

4. **A Daily Record of the Truth:** What thoughts, truths, or observations do you want to record today so that they cannot be erased or forgotten?

_____

_____

_____

_____

_____

_____

Day 254

1. **Gratitude Exercise:** What is one extraordinarily beautiful truth about the world that you noticed today?

    _____

    _____

    _____

2. **Examine Your Actions:** Where have you been challenged today? Where have you compromised the truth or fail to live up to the fullness of justice? What are your struggles and challenges living for the sake of Truth?

    _____

    _____

    _____

3. **Resolution for living in Truth & Freedom:** What concrete thing(s) will you do tomorrow to overcome the lies and live more fully in the truth, no matter the cost?

    _____

    _____

4. **A Daily Record of the Truth:** What thoughts, truths, or observations do you want to record today so that they cannot be erased or forgotten?

    _____

    _____

    _____

    _____

    _____

    _____

Day 255

1. **Gratitude Exercise:** What is one extraordinarily beautiful truth about the world that you noticed today?

    _____

    _____

    _____

2. **Examine Your Actions:** Where have you been challenged today? Where have you compromised the truth or fail to live up to the fullness of justice? What are your struggles and challenges living for the sake of Truth?

    _____

    _____

    _____

3. **Resolution for living in Truth & Freedom:** What concrete thing(s) will you do tomorrow to overcome the lies and live more fully in the truth, no matter the cost?

    _____

    _____

4. **A Daily Record of the Truth:** What thoughts, truths, or observations do you want to record today so that they cannot be erased or forgotten?

    _____

    _____

    _____

    _____

    _____

Day 256

1. **Gratitude Exercise:** What is one extraordinarily beautiful truth about the world that you noticed today?

   _____

   _____

   _____

2. **Examine Your Actions:** Where have you been challenged today? Where have you compromised the truth or fail to live up to the fullness of justice? What are your struggles and challenges living for the sake of Truth?

   _____

   _____

   _____

3. **Resolution for living in Truth & Freedom:** What concrete thing(s) will you do tomorrow to overcome the lies and live more fully in the truth, no matter the cost?

   _____

   _____

4. **A Daily Record of the Truth:** What thoughts, truths, or observations do you want to record today so that they cannot be erased or forgotten?

   _____

   _____

   _____

   _____

   _____

   _____

Day 257

1. **Gratitude Exercise:** What is one extraordinarily beautiful truth about the world that you noticed today?

_____

_____

_____

2. **Examine Your Actions:** Where have you been challenged today? Where have you compromised the truth or fail to live up to the fullness of justice? What are your struggles and challenges living for the sake of Truth?

_____

_____

_____

3. **Resolution for living in Truth & Freedom:** What concrete thing(s) will you do tomorrow to overcome the lies and live more fully in the truth, no matter the cost?

_____

_____

4. **A Daily Record of the Truth:** What thoughts, truths, or observations do you want to record today so that they cannot be erased or forgotten?

_____

_____

_____

_____

_____

Day 258

1. **Gratitude Exercise:** What is one extraordinarily beautiful truth about the world that you noticed today?

   _____

   _____

   _____

2. **Examine Your Actions:** Where have you been challenged today? Where have you compromised the truth or fail to live up to the fullness of justice? What are your struggles and challenges living for the sake of Truth?

   _____

   _____

   _____

3. **Resolution for living in Truth & Freedom:** What concrete thing(s) will you do tomorrow to overcome the lies and live more fully in the truth, no matter the cost?

   _____

   _____

4. **A Daily Record of the Truth:** What thoughts, truths, or observations do you want to record today so that they cannot be erased or forgotten?

   _____

   _____

   _____

   _____

   _____

   _____

Day 259

1. **Gratitude Exercise:** What is one extraordinarily beautiful truth about the world that you noticed today?

_____

_____

_____

2. **Examine Your Actions:** Where have you been challenged today? Where have you compromised the truth or fail to live up to the fullness of justice? What are your struggles and challenges living for the sake of Truth?

_____

_____

_____

3. **Resolution for living in Truth & Freedom:** What concrete thing(s) will you do tomorrow to overcome the lies and live more fully in the truth, no matter the cost?

_____

_____

4. **A Daily Record of the Truth:** What thoughts, truths, or observations do you want to record today so that they cannot be erased or forgotten?

_____

_____

_____

_____

_____

_____

Day 260

1. **Gratitude Exercise:** What is one extraordinarily beautiful truth about the world that you noticed today?

    _____

    _____

    _____

2. **Examine Your Actions:** Where have you been challenged today? Where have you compromised the truth or fail to live up to the fullness of justice? What are your struggles and challenges living for the sake of Truth?

    _____

    _____

    _____

3. **Resolution for living in Truth & Freedom:** What concrete thing(s) will you do tomorrow to overcome the lies and live more fully in the truth, no matter the cost?

    _____

    _____

4. **A Daily Record of the Truth:** What thoughts, truths, or observations do you want to record today so that they cannot be erased or forgotten?

    _____

    _____

    _____

    _____

    _____

    _____

Day 261

1. **Gratitude Exercise:** What is one extraordinarily beautiful truth about the world that you noticed today?

_____

_____

_____

2. **Examine Your Actions:** Where have you been challenged today? Where have you compromised the truth or fail to live up to the fullness of justice? What are your struggles and challenges living for the sake of Truth?

_____

_____

_____

3. **Resolution for living in Truth & Freedom:** What concrete thing(s) will you do tomorrow to overcome the lies and live more fully in the truth, no matter the cost?

_____

_____

4. **A Daily Record of the Truth:** What thoughts, truths, or observations do you want to record today so that they cannot be erased or forgotten?

_____

_____

_____

_____

_____

_____

Day 262

1. **Gratitude Exercise:** What is one extraordinarily beautiful truth about the world that you noticed today?

_____

_____

_____

2. **Examine Your Actions:** Where have you been challenged today? Where have you compromised the truth or fail to live up to the fullness of justice? What are your struggles and challenges living for the sake of Truth?

_____

_____

_____

3. **Resolution for living in Truth & Freedom:** What concrete thing(s) will you do tomorrow to overcome the lies and live more fully in the truth, no matter the cost?

_____

_____

4. **A Daily Record of the Truth:** What thoughts, truths, or observations do you want to record today so that they cannot be erased or forgotten?

_____

_____

_____

_____

_____

_____

Day 263

1. **Gratitude Exercise:** What is one extraordinarily beautiful truth about the world that you noticed today?

_____

_____

_____

2. **Examine Your Actions:** Where have you been challenged today? Where have you compromised the truth or fail to live up to the fullness of justice? What are your struggles and challenges living for the sake of Truth?

_____

_____

_____

3. **Resolution for living in Truth & Freedom:** What concrete thing(s) will you do tomorrow to overcome the lies and live more fully in the truth, no matter the cost?

_____

_____

4. **A Daily Record of the Truth:** What thoughts, truths, or observations do you want to record today so that they cannot be erased or forgotten?

_____

_____

_____

_____

_____

_____

Day 264

1. **Gratitude Exercise:** What is one extraordinarily beautiful truth about the world that you noticed today?

    _____

    _____

    _____

2. **Examine Your Actions:** Where have you been challenged today? Where have you compromised the truth or fail to live up to the fullness of justice? What are your struggles and challenges living for the sake of Truth?

    _____

    _____

    _____

3. **Resolution for living in Truth & Freedom:** What concrete thing(s) will you do tomorrow to overcome the lies and live more fully in the truth, no matter the cost?

    _____

    _____

4. **A Daily Record of the Truth:** What thoughts, truths, or observations do you want to record today so that they cannot be erased or forgotten?

    _____

    _____

    _____

    _____

    _____

    _____

Day 265

1. **Gratitude Exercise:** What is one extraordinarily beautiful truth about the world that you noticed today?

_____

_____

_____

2. **Examine Your Actions:** Where have you been challenged today? Where have you compromised the truth or fail to live up to the fullness of justice? What are your struggles and challenges living for the sake of Truth?

_____

_____

_____

3. **Resolution for living in Truth & Freedom:** What concrete thing(s) will you do tomorrow to overcome the lies and live more fully in the truth, no matter the cost?

_____

_____

4. **A Daily Record of the Truth:** What thoughts, truths, or observations do you want to record today so that they cannot be erased or forgotten?

_____

_____

_____

_____

_____

_____

Day 266

1. **Gratitude Exercise:** What is one extraordinarily beautiful truth about the world that you noticed today?

_____

_____

_____

2. **Examine Your Actions:** Where have you been challenged today? Where have you compromised the truth or fail to live up to the fullness of justice? What are your struggles and challenges living for the sake of Truth?

_____

_____

_____

3. **Resolution for living in Truth & Freedom:** What concrete thing(s) will you do tomorrow to overcome the lies and live more fully in the truth, no matter the cost?

_____

_____

4. **A Daily Record of the Truth:** What thoughts, truths, or observations do you want to record today so that they cannot be erased or forgotten?

_____

_____

_____

_____

_____

Day 267

1. **Gratitude Exercise:** What is one extraordinarily beautiful truth about the world that you noticed today?

_____

_____

_____

2. **Examine Your Actions:** Where have you been challenged today? Where have you compromised the truth or fail to live up to the fullness of justice? What are your struggles and challenges living for the sake of Truth?

_____

_____

_____

3. **Resolution for living in Truth & Freedom:** What concrete thing(s) will you do tomorrow to overcome the lies and live more fully in the truth, no matter the cost?

_____

_____

4. **A Daily Record of the Truth:** What thoughts, truths, or observations do you want to record today so that they cannot be erased or forgotten?

_____

_____

_____

_____

_____

_____

Day 268

1. **Gratitude Exercise:** What is one extraordinarily beautiful truth about the world that you noticed today?

   _____

   _____

   _____

2. **Examine Your Actions:** Where have you been challenged today? Where have you compromised the truth or fail to live up to the fullness of justice? What are your struggles and challenges living for the sake of Truth?

   _____

   _____

   _____

3. **Resolution for living in Truth & Freedom:** What concrete thing(s) will you do tomorrow to overcome the lies and live more fully in the truth, no matter the cost?

   _____

   _____

4. **A Daily Record of the Truth:** What thoughts, truths, or observations do you want to record today so that they cannot be erased or forgotten?

   _____

   _____

   _____

   _____

   _____

Day 269

1. **Gratitude Exercise:** What is one extraordinarily beautiful truth about the world that you noticed today?

_____

_____

_____

2. **Examine Your Actions:** Where have you been challenged today? Where have you compromised the truth or fail to live up to the fullness of justice? What are your struggles and challenges living for the sake of Truth?

_____

_____

_____

3. **Resolution for living in Truth & Freedom:** What concrete thing(s) will you do tomorrow to overcome the lies and live more fully in the truth, no matter the cost?

_____

_____

4. **A Daily Record of the Truth:** What thoughts, truths, or observations do you want to record today so that they cannot be erased or forgotten?

_____

_____

_____

_____

_____

_____

Day 270

1. **Gratitude Exercise:** What is one extraordinarily beautiful truth about the world that you noticed today?

_____

_____

_____

2. **Examine Your Actions:** Where have you been challenged today? Where have you compromised the truth or fail to live up to the fullness of justice? What are your struggles and challenges living for the sake of Truth?

_____

_____

_____

3. **Resolution for living in Truth & Freedom:** What concrete thing(s) will you do tomorrow to overcome the lies and live more fully in the truth, no matter the cost?

_____

_____

4. **A Daily Record of the Truth:** What thoughts, truths, or observations do you want to record today so that they cannot be erased or forgotten?

_____

_____

_____

_____

_____

Day 271

1. **Gratitude Exercise:** What is one extraordinarily beautiful truth about the world that you noticed today?

_____

_____

_____

2. **Examine Your Actions:** Where have you been challenged today? Where have you compromised the truth or fail to live up to the fullness of justice? What are your struggles and challenges living for the sake of Truth?

_____

_____

_____

3. **Resolution for living in Truth & Freedom:** What concrete thing(s) will you do tomorrow to overcome the lies and live more fully in the truth, no matter the cost?

_____

_____

4. **A Daily Record of the Truth:** What thoughts, truths, or observations do you want to record today so that they cannot be erased or forgotten?

_____

_____

_____

_____

_____

_____

Day 272

1. **Gratitude Exercise:** What is one extraordinarily beautiful truth about the world that you noticed today?

_____

_____

_____

2. **Examine Your Actions:** Where have you been challenged today? Where have you compromised the truth or fail to live up to the fullness of justice? What are your struggles and challenges living for the sake of Truth?

_____

_____

_____

3. **Resolution for living in Truth & Freedom:** What concrete thing(s) will you do tomorrow to overcome the lies and live more fully in the truth, no matter the cost?

_____

_____

4. **A Daily Record of the Truth:** What thoughts, truths, or observations do you want to record today so that they cannot be erased or forgotten?

_____

_____

_____

_____

_____

_____

Day 273

1. **Gratitude Exercise:** What is one extraordinarily beautiful truth about the world that you noticed today?

_____

_____

_____

2. **Examine Your Actions:** Where have you been challenged today? Where have you compromised the truth or fail to live up to the fullness of justice? What are your struggles and challenges living for the sake of Truth?

_____

_____

_____

3. **Resolution for living in Truth & Freedom:** What concrete thing(s) will you do tomorrow to overcome the lies and live more fully in the truth, no matter the cost?

_____

_____

4. **A Daily Record of the Truth:** What thoughts, truths, or observations do you want to record today so that they cannot be erased or forgotten?

_____

_____

_____

_____

_____

_____

Day 274

1. **Gratitude Exercise:** What is one extraordinarily beautiful truth about the world that you noticed today?

    _____

    _____

    _____

2. **Examine Your Actions:** Where have you been challenged today? Where have you compromised the truth or fail to live up to the fullness of justice? What are your struggles and challenges living for the sake of Truth?

    _____

    _____

    _____

3. **Resolution for living in Truth & Freedom:** What concrete thing(s) will you do tomorrow to overcome the lies and live more fully in the truth, no matter the cost?

    _____

    _____

4. **A Daily Record of the Truth:** What thoughts, truths, or observations do you want to record today so that they cannot be erased or forgotten?

    _____

    _____

    _____

    _____

    _____

    _____

Day 275

1. **Gratitude Exercise:** What is one extraordinarily beautiful truth about the world that you noticed today?

_____

_____

_____

2. **Examine Your Actions:** Where have you been challenged today? Where have you compromised the truth or fail to live up to the fullness of justice? What are your struggles and challenges living for the sake of Truth?

_____

_____

_____

3. **Resolution for living in Truth & Freedom:** What concrete thing(s) will you do tomorrow to overcome the lies and live more fully in the truth, no matter the cost?

_____

_____

4. **A Daily Record of the Truth:** What thoughts, truths, or observations do you want to record today so that they cannot be erased or forgotten?

_____

_____

_____

_____

_____

_____

Day 276

1. **Gratitude Exercise:** What is one extraordinarily beautiful truth about the world that you noticed today?

_____

_____

_____

2. **Examine Your Actions:** Where have you been challenged today? Where have you compromised the truth or fail to live up to the fullness of justice? What are your struggles and challenges living for the sake of Truth?

_____

_____

_____

3. **Resolution for living in Truth & Freedom:** What concrete thing(s) will you do tomorrow to overcome the lies and live more fully in the truth, no matter the cost?

_____

_____

4. **A Daily Record of the Truth:** What thoughts, truths, or observations do you want to record today so that they cannot be erased or forgotten?

_____

_____

_____

_____

_____

_____

Day 277

1. **Gratitude Exercise:** What is one extraordinarily beautiful truth about the world that you noticed today?

_____

_____

_____

2. **Examine Your Actions:** Where have you been challenged today? Where have you compromised the truth or fail to live up to the fullness of justice? What are your struggles and challenges living for the sake of Truth?

_____

_____

_____

3. **Resolution for living in Truth & Freedom:** What concrete thing(s) will you do tomorrow to overcome the lies and live more fully in the truth, no matter the cost?

_____

_____

4. **A Daily Record of the Truth:** What thoughts, truths, or observations do you want to record today so that they cannot be erased or forgotten?

_____

_____

_____

_____

_____

Day 278

1. **Gratitude Exercise:** What is one extraordinarily beautiful truth about the world that you noticed today?

---

2. **Examine Your Actions:** Where have you been challenged today? Where have you compromised the truth or fail to live up to the fullness of justice? What are your struggles and challenges living for the sake of Truth?

---

3. **Resolution for living in Truth & Freedom:** What concrete thing(s) will you do tomorrow to overcome the lies and live more fully in the truth, no matter the cost?

---

4. **A Daily Record of the Truth:** What thoughts, truths, or observations do you want to record today so that they cannot be erased or forgotten?

Day 279

1. **Gratitude Exercise:** What is one extraordinarily beautiful truth about the world that you noticed today?

_____

_____

_____

2. **Examine Your Actions:** Where have you been challenged today? Where have you compromised the truth or fail to live up to the fullness of justice? What are your struggles and challenges living for the sake of Truth?

_____

_____

_____

3. **Resolution for living in Truth & Freedom:** What concrete thing(s) will you do tomorrow to overcome the lies and live more fully in the truth, no matter the cost?

_____

_____

4. **A Daily Record of the Truth:** What thoughts, truths, or observations do you want to record today so that they cannot be erased or forgotten?

_____

_____

_____

_____

_____

_____

Day 280

1. **Gratitude Exercise:** What is one extraordinarily beautiful truth about the world that you noticed today?

_____

_____

_____

2. **Examine Your Actions:** Where have you been challenged today? Where have you compromised the truth or fail to live up to the fullness of justice? What are your struggles and challenges living for the sake of Truth?

_____

_____

_____

3. **Resolution for living in Truth & Freedom:** What concrete thing(s) will you do tomorrow to overcome the lies and live more fully in the truth, no matter the cost?

_____

_____

4. **A Daily Record of the Truth:** What thoughts, truths, or observations do you want to record today so that they cannot be erased or forgotten?

_____

_____

_____

_____

_____

_____

Day 281

1. **Gratitude Exercise:** What is one extraordinarily beautiful truth about the world that you noticed today?

_____

_____

_____

2. **Examine Your Actions:** Where have you been challenged today? Where have you compromised the truth or fail to live up to the fullness of justice? What are your struggles and challenges living for the sake of Truth?

_____

_____

_____

3. **Resolution for living in Truth & Freedom:** What concrete thing(s) will you do tomorrow to overcome the lies and live more fully in the truth, no matter the cost?

_____

_____

4. **A Daily Record of the Truth:** What thoughts, truths, or observations do you want to record today so that they cannot be erased or forgotten?

_____

_____

_____

_____

_____

_____

Day 282

1. **Gratitude Exercise:** What is one extraordinarily beautiful truth about the world that you noticed today?

_____

_____

_____

2. **Examine Your Actions:** Where have you been challenged today? Where have you compromised the truth or fail to live up to the fullness of justice? What are your struggles and challenges living for the sake of Truth?

_____

_____

_____

3. **Resolution for living in Truth & Freedom:** What concrete thing(s) will you do tomorrow to overcome the lies and live more fully in the truth, no matter the cost?

_____

_____

4. **A Daily Record of the Truth:** What thoughts, truths, or observations do you want to record today so that they cannot be erased or forgotten?

_____

_____

_____

_____

_____

Day 283

1. **Gratitude Exercise:** What is one extraordinarily beautiful truth about the world that you noticed today?

_____

_____

_____

2. **Examine Your Actions:** Where have you been challenged today? Where have you compromised the truth or fail to live up to the fullness of justice? What are your struggles and challenges living for the sake of Truth?

_____

_____

_____

3. **Resolution for living in Truth & Freedom:** What concrete thing(s) will you do tomorrow to overcome the lies and live more fully in the truth, no matter the cost?

_____

_____

4. **A Daily Record of the Truth:** What thoughts, truths, or observations do you want to record today so that they cannot be erased or forgotten?

_____

_____

_____

_____

_____

_____

Day 284

1. **Gratitude Exercise:** What is one extraordinarily beautiful truth about the world that you noticed today?

    _____

    _____

    _____

2. **Examine Your Actions:** Where have you been challenged today? Where have you compromised the truth or fail to live up to the fullness of justice? What are your struggles and challenges living for the sake of Truth?

    _____

    _____

    _____

3. **Resolution for living in Truth & Freedom:** What concrete thing(s) will you do tomorrow to overcome the lies and live more fully in the truth, no matter the cost?

    _____

    _____

4. **A Daily Record of the Truth:** What thoughts, truths, or observations do you want to record today so that they cannot be erased or forgotten?

    _____

    _____

    _____

    _____

    _____

    _____

Day 285

1. **Gratitude Exercise:** What is one extraordinarily beautiful truth about the world that you noticed today?

_____

_____

_____

2. **Examine Your Actions:** Where have you been challenged today? Where have you compromised the truth or fail to live up to the fullness of justice? What are your struggles and challenges living for the sake of Truth?

_____

_____

_____

3. **Resolution for living in Truth & Freedom:** What concrete thing(s) will you do tomorrow to overcome the lies and live more fully in the truth, no matter the cost?

_____

_____

4. **A Daily Record of the Truth:** What thoughts, truths, or observations do you want to record today so that they cannot be erased or forgotten?

_____

_____

_____

_____

_____

Day 286

1. **Gratitude Exercise:** What is one extraordinarily beautiful truth about the world that you noticed today?

_____

_____

_____

2. **Examine Your Actions:** Where have you been challenged today? Where have you compromised the truth or fail to live up to the fullness of justice? What are your struggles and challenges living for the sake of Truth?

_____

_____

_____

3. **Resolution for living in Truth & Freedom:** What concrete thing(s) will you do tomorrow to overcome the lies and live more fully in the truth, no matter the cost?

_____

_____

4. **A Daily Record of the Truth:** What thoughts, truths, or observations do you want to record today so that they cannot be erased or forgotten?

_____

_____

_____

_____

_____

_____

Day 287

1. **Gratitude Exercise:** What is one extraordinarily beautiful truth about the world that you noticed today?

_____

_____

_____

2. **Examine Your Actions:** Where have you been challenged today? Where have you compromised the truth or fail to live up to the fullness of justice? What are your struggles and challenges living for the sake of Truth?

_____

_____

_____

3. **Resolution for living in Truth & Freedom:** What concrete thing(s) will you do tomorrow to overcome the lies and live more fully in the truth, no matter the cost?

_____

_____

4. **A Daily Record of the Truth:** What thoughts, truths, or observations do you want to record today so that they cannot be erased or forgotten?

_____

_____

_____

_____

_____

_____

Day 288

1. **Gratitude Exercise:** What is one extraordinarily beautiful truth about the world that you noticed today?

_____

_____

_____

2. **Examine Your Actions:** Where have you been challenged today? Where have you compromised the truth or fail to live up to the fullness of justice? What are your struggles and challenges living for the sake of Truth?

_____

_____

_____

3. **Resolution for living in Truth & Freedom:** What concrete thing(s) will you do tomorrow to overcome the lies and live more fully in the truth, no matter the cost?

_____

_____

4. **A Daily Record of the Truth:** What thoughts, truths, or observations do you want to record today so that they cannot be erased or forgotten?

_____

_____

_____

_____

_____

_____

Day 289

1. **Gratitude Exercise:** What is one extraordinarily beautiful truth about the world that you noticed today?

_____

_____

_____

2. **Examine Your Actions:** Where have you been challenged today? Where have you compromised the truth or fail to live up to the fullness of justice? What are your struggles and challenges living for the sake of Truth?

_____

_____

_____

3. **Resolution for living in Truth & Freedom:** What concrete thing(s) will you do tomorrow to overcome the lies and live more fully in the truth, no matter the cost?

_____

_____

4. **A Daily Record of the Truth:** What thoughts, truths, or observations do you want to record today so that they cannot be erased or forgotten?

_____

_____

_____

_____

_____

_____

Day 290

1. **Gratitude Exercise:** What is one extraordinarily beautiful truth about the world that you noticed today?

_____

_____

_____

2. **Examine Your Actions:** Where have you been challenged today? Where have you compromised the truth or fail to live up to the fullness of justice? What are your struggles and challenges living for the sake of Truth?

_____

_____

_____

3. **Resolution for living in Truth & Freedom:** What concrete thing(s) will you do tomorrow to overcome the lies and live more fully in the truth, no matter the cost?

_____

_____

4. **A Daily Record of the Truth:** What thoughts, truths, or observations do you want to record today so that they cannot be erased or forgotten?

_____

_____

_____

_____

_____

_____

Day 291

1. **Gratitude Exercise:** What is one extraordinarily beautiful truth about the world that you noticed today?

_____

_____

_____

2. **Examine Your Actions:** Where have you been challenged today? Where have you compromised the truth or fail to live up to the fullness of justice? What are your struggles and challenges living for the sake of Truth?

_____

_____

_____

3. **Resolution for living in Truth & Freedom:** What concrete thing(s) will you do tomorrow to overcome the lies and live more fully in the truth, no matter the cost?

_____

_____

4. **A Daily Record of the Truth:** What thoughts, truths, or observations do you want to record today so that they cannot be erased or forgotten?

_____

_____

_____

_____

_____

Day 292

1. **Gratitude Exercise:** What is one extraordinarily beautiful truth about the world that you noticed today?

———————————————————————————

———————————————————————————

———————————————————————————

2. **Examine Your Actions:** Where have you been challenged today? Where have you compromised the truth or fail to live up to the fullness of justice? What are your struggles and challenges living for the sake of Truth?

———————————————————————————

———————————————————————————

———————————————————————————

3. **Resolution for living in Truth & Freedom:** What concrete thing(s) will you do tomorrow to overcome the lies and live more fully in the truth, no matter the cost?

———————————————————————————

———————————————————————————

4. **A Daily Record of the Truth:** What thoughts, truths, or observations do you want to record today so that they cannot be erased or forgotten?

———————————————————————————

———————————————————————————

———————————————————————————

———————————————————————————

———————————————————————————

———————————————————————————

Day 293

1. **Gratitude Exercise:** What is one extraordinarily beautiful truth about the world that you noticed today?

_____

_____

_____

2. **Examine Your Actions:** Where have you been challenged today? Where have you compromised the truth or fail to live up to the fullness of justice? What are your struggles and challenges living for the sake of Truth?

_____

_____

_____

3. **Resolution for living in Truth & Freedom:** What concrete thing(s) will you do tomorrow to overcome the lies and live more fully in the truth, no matter the cost?

_____

_____

4. **A Daily Record of the Truth:** What thoughts, truths, or observations do you want to record today so that they cannot be erased or forgotten?

_____

_____

_____

_____

_____

_____

Day 294

1. **Gratitude Exercise:** What is one extraordinarily beautiful truth about the world that you noticed today?

_____

_____

_____

2. **Examine Your Actions:** Where have you been challenged today? Where have you compromised the truth or fail to live up to the fullness of justice? What are your struggles and challenges living for the sake of Truth?

_____

_____

_____

3. **Resolution for living in Truth & Freedom:** What concrete thing(s) will you do tomorrow to overcome the lies and live more fully in the truth, no matter the cost?

_____

_____

4. **A Daily Record of the Truth:** What thoughts, truths, or observations do you want to record today so that they cannot be erased or forgotten?

_____

_____

_____

_____

_____

_____

Day 295

1. **Gratitude Exercise:** What is one extraordinarily beautiful truth about the world that you noticed today?

_____

_____

_____

2. **Examine Your Actions:** Where have you been challenged today? Where have you compromised the truth or fail to live up to the fullness of justice? What are your struggles and challenges living for the sake of Truth?

_____

_____

_____

3. **Resolution for living in Truth & Freedom:** What concrete thing(s) will you do tomorrow to overcome the lies and live more fully in the truth, no matter the cost?

_____

_____

4. **A Daily Record of the Truth:** What thoughts, truths, or observations do you want to record today so that they cannot be erased or forgotten?

_____

_____

_____

_____

_____

_____

Day 296

1. **Gratitude Exercise:** What is one extraordinarily beautiful truth about the world that you noticed today?

_____

_____

_____

2. **Examine Your Actions:** Where have you been challenged today? Where have you compromised the truth or fail to live up to the fullness of justice? What are your struggles and challenges living for the sake of Truth?

_____

_____

_____

3. **Resolution for living in Truth & Freedom:** What concrete thing(s) will you do tomorrow to overcome the lies and live more fully in the truth, no matter the cost?

_____

_____

4. **A Daily Record of the Truth:** What thoughts, truths, or observations do you want to record today so that they cannot be erased or forgotten?

_____

_____

_____

_____

_____

_____

Day 297

1. **Gratitude Exercise:** What is one extraordinarily beautiful truth about the world that you noticed today?

_____

_____

_____

2. **Examine Your Actions:** Where have you been challenged today? Where have you compromised the truth or fail to live up to the fullness of justice? What are your struggles and challenges living for the sake of Truth?

_____

_____

_____

3. **Resolution for living in Truth & Freedom:** What concrete thing(s) will you do tomorrow to overcome the lies and live more fully in the truth, no matter the cost?

_____

_____

4. **A Daily Record of the Truth:** What thoughts, truths, or observations do you want to record today so that they cannot be erased or forgotten?

_____

_____

_____

_____

_____

Day 298

1. **Gratitude Exercise:** What is one extraordinarily beautiful truth about the world that you noticed today?

_____

_____

_____

2. **Examine Your Actions:** Where have you been challenged today? Where have you compromised the truth or fail to live up to the fullness of justice? What are your struggles and challenges living for the sake of Truth?

_____

_____

_____

3. **Resolution for living in Truth & Freedom:** What concrete thing(s) will you do tomorrow to overcome the lies and live more fully in the truth, no matter the cost?

_____

_____

4. **A Daily Record of the Truth:** What thoughts, truths, or observations do you want to record today so that they cannot be erased or forgotten?

_____

_____

_____

_____

_____

_____

Day 299

1. **Gratitude Exercise:** What is one extraordinarily beautiful truth about the world that you noticed today?

_____

_____

_____

2. **Examine Your Actions:** Where have you been challenged today? Where have you compromised the truth or fail to live up to the fullness of justice? What are your struggles and challenges living for the sake of Truth?

_____

_____

_____

3. **Resolution for living in Truth & Freedom:** What concrete thing(s) will you do tomorrow to overcome the lies and live more fully in the truth, no matter the cost?

_____

_____

4. **A Daily Record of the Truth:** What thoughts, truths, or observations do you want to record today so that they cannot be erased or forgotten?

_____

_____

_____

_____

_____

Day 300

1. **Gratitude Exercise:** What is one extraordinarily beautiful truth about the world that you noticed today?

_____

_____

_____

2. **Examine Your Actions:** Where have you been challenged today? Where have you compromised the truth or fail to live up to the fullness of justice? What are your struggles and challenges living for the sake of Truth?

_____

_____

_____

3. **Resolution for living in Truth & Freedom:** What concrete thing(s) will you do tomorrow to overcome the lies and live more fully in the truth, no matter the cost?

_____

_____

4. **A Daily Record of the Truth:** What thoughts, truths, or observations do you want to record today so that they cannot be erased or forgotten?

_____

_____

_____

_____

_____

_____

Day 301

1. **Gratitude Exercise:** What is one extraordinarily beautiful truth about the world that you noticed today?

_____

_____

_____

2. **Examine Your Actions:** Where have you been challenged today? Where have you compromised the truth or fail to live up to the fullness of justice? What are your struggles and challenges living for the sake of Truth?

_____

_____

_____

3. **Resolution for living in Truth & Freedom:** What concrete thing(s) will you do tomorrow to overcome the lies and live more fully in the truth, no matter the cost?

_____

_____

4. **A Daily Record of the Truth:** What thoughts, truths, or observations do you want to record today so that they cannot be erased or forgotten?

_____

_____

_____

_____

_____

_____

Day 302

1. **Gratitude Exercise:** What is one extraordinarily beautiful truth about the world that you noticed today?

_____

_____

_____

2. **Examine Your Actions:** Where have you been challenged today? Where have you compromised the truth or fail to live up to the fullness of justice? What are your struggles and challenges living for the sake of Truth?

_____

_____

_____

3. **Resolution for living in Truth & Freedom:** What concrete thing(s) will you do tomorrow to overcome the lies and live more fully in the truth, no matter the cost?

_____

_____

4. **A Daily Record of the Truth:** What thoughts, truths, or observations do you want to record today so that they cannot be erased or forgotten?

_____

_____

_____

_____

_____

Day 303

1. **Gratitude Exercise:** What is one extraordinarily beautiful truth about the world that you noticed today?

_____

_____

_____

2. **Examine Your Actions:** Where have you been challenged today? Where have you compromised the truth or fail to live up to the fullness of justice? What are your struggles and challenges living for the sake of Truth?

_____

_____

_____

3. **Resolution for living in Truth & Freedom:** What concrete thing(s) will you do tomorrow to overcome the lies and live more fully in the truth, no matter the cost?

_____

_____

4. **A Daily Record of the Truth:** What thoughts, truths, or observations do you want to record today so that they cannot be erased or forgotten?

_____

_____

_____

_____

_____

_____

Day 304

1. **Gratitude Exercise:** What is one extraordinarily beautiful truth about the world that you noticed today?

   _____

   _____

   _____

2. **Examine Your Actions:** Where have you been challenged today? Where have you compromised the truth or fail to live up to the fullness of justice? What are your struggles and challenges living for the sake of Truth?

   _____

   _____

   _____

3. **Resolution for living in Truth & Freedom:** What concrete thing(s) will you do tomorrow to overcome the lies and live more fully in the truth, no matter the cost?

   _____

   _____

4. **A Daily Record of the Truth:** What thoughts, truths, or observations do you want to record today so that they cannot be erased or forgotten?

   _____

   _____

   _____

   _____

   _____

   _____

Day 305

1. **Gratitude Exercise:** What is one extraordinarily beautiful truth about the world that you noticed today?

_____

_____

_____

2. **Examine Your Actions:** Where have you been challenged today? Where have you compromised the truth or fail to live up to the fullness of justice? What are your struggles and challenges living for the sake of Truth?

_____

_____

_____

3. **Resolution for living in Truth & Freedom:** What concrete thing(s) will you do tomorrow to overcome the lies and live more fully in the truth, no matter the cost?

_____

_____

4. **A Daily Record of the Truth:** What thoughts, truths, or observations do you want to record today so that they cannot be erased or forgotten?

_____

_____

_____

_____

_____

_____

Day 306

1. **Gratitude Exercise:** What is one extraordinarily beautiful truth about the world that you noticed today?

_____

_____

_____

2. **Examine Your Actions:** Where have you been challenged today? Where have you compromised the truth or fail to live up to the fullness of justice? What are your struggles and challenges living for the sake of Truth?

_____

_____

_____

3. **Resolution for living in Truth & Freedom:** What concrete thing(s) will you do tomorrow to overcome the lies and live more fully in the truth, no matter the cost?

_____

_____

4. **A Daily Record of the Truth:** What thoughts, truths, or observations do you want to record today so that they cannot be erased or forgotten?

_____

_____

_____

_____

_____

_____

Day 307

1. **Gratitude Exercise:** What is one extraordinarily beautiful truth about the world that you noticed today?

_____

_____

_____

2. **Examine Your Actions:** Where have you been challenged today? Where have you compromised the truth or fail to live up to the fullness of justice? What are your struggles and challenges living for the sake of Truth?

_____

_____

_____

3. **Resolution for living in Truth & Freedom:** What concrete thing(s) will you do tomorrow to overcome the lies and live more fully in the truth, no matter the cost?

_____

_____

4. **A Daily Record of the Truth:** What thoughts, truths, or observations do you want to record today so that they cannot be erased or forgotten?

_____

_____

_____

_____

_____

Day 308

1. **Gratitude Exercise:** What is one extraordinarily beautiful truth about the world that you noticed today?

    _____

    _____

    _____

2. **Examine Your Actions:** Where have you been challenged today? Where have you compromised the truth or fail to live up to the fullness of justice? What are your struggles and challenges living for the sake of Truth?

    _____

    _____

    _____

3. **Resolution for living in Truth & Freedom:** What concrete thing(s) will you do tomorrow to overcome the lies and live more fully in the truth, no matter the cost?

    _____

    _____

4. **A Daily Record of the Truth:** What thoughts, truths, or observations do you want to record today so that they cannot be erased or forgotten?

    _____

    _____

    _____

    _____

    _____

    _____

Day 309

1. **Gratitude Exercise:** What is one extraordinarily beautiful truth about the world that you noticed today?

_____

_____

_____

2. **Examine Your Actions:** Where have you been challenged today? Where have you compromised the truth or fail to live up to the fullness of justice? What are your struggles and challenges living for the sake of Truth?

_____

_____

_____

3. **Resolution for living in Truth & Freedom:** What concrete thing(s) will you do tomorrow to overcome the lies and live more fully in the truth, no matter the cost?

_____

_____

4. **A Daily Record of the Truth:** What thoughts, truths, or observations do you want to record today so that they cannot be erased or forgotten?

_____

_____

_____

_____

_____

_____

Day 310

1. **Gratitude Exercise:** What is one extraordinarily beautiful truth about the world that you noticed today?

_____

_____

_____

2. **Examine Your Actions:** Where have you been challenged today? Where have you compromised the truth or fail to live up to the fullness of justice? What are your struggles and challenges living for the sake of Truth?

_____

_____

_____

3. **Resolution for living in Truth & Freedom:** What concrete thing(s) will you do tomorrow to overcome the lies and live more fully in the truth, no matter the cost?

_____

_____

4. **A Daily Record of the Truth:** What thoughts, truths, or observations do you want to record today so that they cannot be erased or forgotten?

_____

_____

_____

_____

_____

_____

Day 311

1. **Gratitude Exercise:** What is one extraordinarily beautiful truth about the world that you noticed today?

_____

_____

_____

2. **Examine Your Actions:** Where have you been challenged today? Where have you compromised the truth or fail to live up to the fullness of justice? What are your struggles and challenges living for the sake of Truth?

_____

_____

_____

3. **Resolution for living in Truth & Freedom:** What concrete thing(s) will you do tomorrow to overcome the lies and live more fully in the truth, no matter the cost?

_____

_____

4. **A Daily Record of the Truth:** What thoughts, truths, or observations do you want to record today so that they cannot be erased or forgotten?

_____

_____

_____

_____

_____

Day 312

1. **Gratitude Exercise:** What is one extraordinarily beautiful truth about the world that you noticed today?

   _____

   _____

   _____

2. **Examine Your Actions:** Where have you been challenged today? Where have you compromised the truth or fail to live up to the fullness of justice? What are your struggles and challenges living for the sake of Truth?

   _____

   _____

   _____

3. **Resolution for living in Truth & Freedom:** What concrete thing(s) will you do tomorrow to overcome the lies and live more fully in the truth, no matter the cost?

   _____

   _____

4. **A Daily Record of the Truth:** What thoughts, truths, or observations do you want to record today so that they cannot be erased or forgotten?

   _____

   _____

   _____

   _____

   _____

   _____

Day 313

1. **Gratitude Exercise:** What is one extraordinarily beautiful truth about the world that you noticed today?

_____

_____

_____

2. **Examine Your Actions:** Where have you been challenged today? Where have you compromised the truth or fail to live up to the fullness of justice? What are your struggles and challenges living for the sake of Truth?

_____

_____

_____

3. **Resolution for living in Truth & Freedom:** What concrete thing(s) will you do tomorrow to overcome the lies and live more fully in the truth, no matter the cost?

_____

_____

4. **A Daily Record of the Truth:** What thoughts, truths, or observations do you want to record today so that they cannot be erased or forgotten?

_____

_____

_____

_____

_____

_____

Day 314

1. **Gratitude Exercise:** What is one extraordinarily beautiful truth about the world that you noticed today?

_____

_____

_____

2. **Examine Your Actions:** Where have you been challenged today? Where have you compromised the truth or fail to live up to the fullness of justice? What are your struggles and challenges living for the sake of Truth?

_____

_____

_____

3. **Resolution for living in Truth & Freedom:** What concrete thing(s) will you do tomorrow to overcome the lies and live more fully in the truth, no matter the cost?

_____

_____

4. **A Daily Record of the Truth:** What thoughts, truths, or observations do you want to record today so that they cannot be erased or forgotten?

_____

_____

_____

_____

_____

_____

Day 315

1. **Gratitude Exercise:** What is one extraordinarily beautiful truth about the world that you noticed today?

    _____

    _____

    _____

2. **Examine Your Actions:** Where have you been challenged today? Where have you compromised the truth or fail to live up to the fullness of justice? What are your struggles and challenges living for the sake of Truth?

    _____

    _____

    _____

3. **Resolution for living in Truth & Freedom:** What concrete thing(s) will you do tomorrow to overcome the lies and live more fully in the truth, no matter the cost?

    _____

    _____

4. **A Daily Record of the Truth:** What thoughts, truths, or observations do you want to record today so that they cannot be erased or forgotten?

    _____

    _____

    _____

    _____

    _____

    _____

Day 316

1. **Gratitude Exercise:** What is one extraordinarily beautiful truth about the world that you noticed today?

_____

_____

_____

2. **Examine Your Actions:** Where have you been challenged today? Where have you compromised the truth or fail to live up to the fullness of justice? What are your struggles and challenges living for the sake of Truth?

_____

_____

_____

3. **Resolution for living in Truth & Freedom:** What concrete thing(s) will you do tomorrow to overcome the lies and live more fully in the truth, no matter the cost?

_____

_____

4. **A Daily Record of the Truth:** What thoughts, truths, or observations do you want to record today so that they cannot be erased or forgotten?

_____

_____

_____

_____

_____

_____

Day 317

1. **Gratitude Exercise:** What is one extraordinarily beautiful truth about the world that you noticed today?

_____

_____

_____

2. **Examine Your Actions:** Where have you been challenged today? Where have you compromised the truth or fail to live up to the fullness of justice? What are your struggles and challenges living for the sake of Truth?

_____

_____

_____

3. **Resolution for living in Truth & Freedom:** What concrete thing(s) will you do tomorrow to overcome the lies and live more fully in the truth, no matter the cost?

_____

_____

4. **A Daily Record of the Truth:** What thoughts, truths, or observations do you want to record today so that they cannot be erased or forgotten?

_____

_____

_____

_____

_____

_____

Day 318

1. **Gratitude Exercise:** What is one extraordinarily beautiful truth about the world that you noticed today?

   _____

   _____

   _____

2. **Examine Your Actions:** Where have you been challenged today? Where have you compromised the truth or fail to live up to the fullness of justice? What are your struggles and challenges living for the sake of Truth?

   _____

   _____

   _____

3. **Resolution for living in Truth & Freedom:** What concrete thing(s) will you do tomorrow to overcome the lies and live more fully in the truth, no matter the cost?

   _____

   _____

4. **A Daily Record of the Truth:** What thoughts, truths, or observations do you want to record today so that they cannot be erased or forgotten?

   _____

   _____

   _____

   _____

   _____

Day 319

1. **Gratitude Exercise:** What is one extraordinarily beautiful truth about the world that you noticed today?

_____

_____

_____

2. **Examine Your Actions:** Where have you been challenged today? Where have you compromised the truth or fail to live up to the fullness of justice? What are your struggles and challenges living for the sake of Truth?

_____

_____

_____

3. **Resolution for living in Truth & Freedom:** What concrete thing(s) will you do tomorrow to overcome the lies and live more fully in the truth, no matter the cost?

_____

_____

4. **A Daily Record of the Truth:** What thoughts, truths, or observations do you want to record today so that they cannot be erased or forgotten?

_____

_____

_____

_____

_____

_____

Day 320

1. **Gratitude Exercise:** What is one extraordinarily beautiful truth about the world that you noticed today?

_____

_____

_____

2. **Examine Your Actions:** Where have you been challenged today? Where have you compromised the truth or fail to live up to the fullness of justice? What are your struggles and challenges living for the sake of Truth?

_____

_____

_____

3. **Resolution for living in Truth & Freedom:** What concrete thing(s) will you do tomorrow to overcome the lies and live more fully in the truth, no matter the cost?

_____

_____

4. **A Daily Record of the Truth:** What thoughts, truths, or observations do you want to record today so that they cannot be erased or forgotten?

_____

_____

_____

_____

_____

_____

Day 321

1. **Gratitude Exercise:** What is one extraordinarily beautiful truth about the world that you noticed today?

    _____

    _____

    _____

2. **Examine Your Actions:** Where have you been challenged today? Where have you compromised the truth or fail to live up to the fullness of justice? What are your struggles and challenges living for the sake of Truth?

    _____

    _____

    _____

3. **Resolution for living in Truth & Freedom:** What concrete thing(s) will you do tomorrow to overcome the lies and live more fully in the truth, no matter the cost?

    _____

    _____

4. **A Daily Record of the Truth:** What thoughts, truths, or observations do you want to record today so that they cannot be erased or forgotten?

    _____

    _____

    _____

    _____

    _____

Day 322

1. **Gratitude Exercise:** What is one extraordinarily beautiful truth about the world that you noticed today?

_____

_____

_____

2. **Examine Your Actions:** Where have you been challenged today? Where have you compromised the truth or fail to live up to the fullness of justice? What are your struggles and challenges living for the sake of Truth?

_____

_____

_____

3. **Resolution for living in Truth & Freedom:** What concrete thing(s) will you do tomorrow to overcome the lies and live more fully in the truth, no matter the cost?

_____

_____

4. **A Daily Record of the Truth:** What thoughts, truths, or observations do you want to record today so that they cannot be erased or forgotten?

_____

_____

_____

_____

_____

_____

Day 323

1. **Gratitude Exercise:** What is one extraordinarily beautiful truth about the world that you noticed today?

_____

_____

_____

2. **Examine Your Actions:** Where have you been challenged today? Where have you compromised the truth or fail to live up to the fullness of justice? What are your struggles and challenges living for the sake of Truth?

_____

_____

_____

3. **Resolution for living in Truth & Freedom:** What concrete thing(s) will you do tomorrow to overcome the lies and live more fully in the truth, no matter the cost?

_____

_____

4. **A Daily Record of the Truth:** What thoughts, truths, or observations do you want to record today so that they cannot be erased or forgotten?

_____

_____

_____

_____

_____

_____

Day 324

1. **Gratitude Exercise:** What is one extraordinarily beautiful truth about the world that you noticed today?

   _____

   _____

   _____

2. **Examine Your Actions:** Where have you been challenged today? Where have you compromised the truth or fail to live up to the fullness of justice? What are your struggles and challenges living for the sake of Truth?

   _____

   _____

   _____

3. **Resolution for living in Truth & Freedom:** What concrete thing(s) will you do tomorrow to overcome the lies and live more fully in the truth, no matter the cost?

   _____

   _____

4. **A Daily Record of the Truth:** What thoughts, truths, or observations do you want to record today so that they cannot be erased or forgotten?

   _____

   _____

   _____

   _____

   _____

   _____

Day 325

1. **Gratitude Exercise:** What is one extraordinarily beautiful truth about the world that you noticed today?

_____

_____

_____

2. **Examine Your Actions:** Where have you been challenged today? Where have you compromised the truth or fail to live up to the fullness of justice? What are your struggles and challenges living for the sake of Truth?

_____

_____

_____

3. **Resolution for living in Truth & Freedom:** What concrete thing(s) will you do tomorrow to overcome the lies and live more fully in the truth, no matter the cost?

_____

_____

4. **A Daily Record of the Truth:** What thoughts, truths, or observations do you want to record today so that they cannot be erased or forgotten?

_____

_____

_____

_____

_____

Day 326

1. **Gratitude Exercise:** What is one extraordinarily beautiful truth about the world that you noticed today?

_____

_____

_____

2. **Examine Your Actions:** Where have you been challenged today? Where have you compromised the truth or fail to live up to the fullness of justice? What are your struggles and challenges living for the sake of Truth?

_____

_____

_____

3. **Resolution for living in Truth & Freedom:** What concrete thing(s) will you do tomorrow to overcome the lies and live more fully in the truth, no matter the cost?

_____

_____

4. **A Daily Record of the Truth:** What thoughts, truths, or observations do you want to record today so that they cannot be erased or forgotten?

_____

_____

_____

_____

_____

_____

Day 327

1. **Gratitude Exercise:** What is one extraordinarily beautiful truth about the world that you noticed today?

_____

_____

_____

2. **Examine Your Actions:** Where have you been challenged today? Where have you compromised the truth or fail to live up to the fullness of justice? What are your struggles and challenges living for the sake of Truth?

_____

_____

_____

3. **Resolution for living in Truth & Freedom:** What concrete thing(s) will you do tomorrow to overcome the lies and live more fully in the truth, no matter the cost?

_____

_____

4. **A Daily Record of the Truth:** What thoughts, truths, or observations do you want to record today so that they cannot be erased or forgotten?

_____

_____

_____

_____

_____

Day 328

1. **Gratitude Exercise:** What is one extraordinarily beautiful truth about the world that you noticed today?

_____

_____

_____

2. **Examine Your Actions:** Where have you been challenged today? Where have you compromised the truth or fail to live up to the fullness of justice? What are your struggles and challenges living for the sake of Truth?

_____

_____

_____

3. **Resolution for living in Truth & Freedom:** What concrete thing(s) will you do tomorrow to overcome the lies and live more fully in the truth, no matter the cost?

_____

_____

4. **A Daily Record of the Truth:** What thoughts, truths, or observations do you want to record today so that they cannot be erased or forgotten?

_____

_____

_____

_____

_____

_____

Day 329

1. **Gratitude Exercise:** What is one extraordinarily beautiful truth about the world that you noticed today?

_____

_____

_____

2. **Examine Your Actions:** Where have you been challenged today? Where have you compromised the truth or fail to live up to the fullness of justice? What are your struggles and challenges living for the sake of Truth?

_____

_____

_____

3. **Resolution for living in Truth & Freedom:** What concrete thing(s) will you do tomorrow to overcome the lies and live more fully in the truth, no matter the cost?

_____

_____

4. **A Daily Record of the Truth:** What thoughts, truths, or observations do you want to record today so that they cannot be erased or forgotten?

_____

_____

_____

_____

_____

_____

Day 330

1. **Gratitude Exercise:** What is one extraordinarily beautiful truth about the world that you noticed today?

_____

_____

_____

2. **Examine Your Actions:** Where have you been challenged today? Where have you compromised the truth or fail to live up to the fullness of justice? What are your struggles and challenges living for the sake of Truth?

_____

_____

_____

3. **Resolution for living in Truth & Freedom:** What concrete thing(s) will you do tomorrow to overcome the lies and live more fully in the truth, no matter the cost?

_____

_____

4. **A Daily Record of the Truth:** What thoughts, truths, or observations do you want to record today so that they cannot be erased or forgotten?

_____

_____

_____

_____

_____

_____

Day 331

1. **Gratitude Exercise:** What is one extraordinarily beautiful truth about the world that you noticed today?

_____

_____

_____

2. **Examine Your Actions:** Where have you been challenged today? Where have you compromised the truth or fail to live up to the fullness of justice? What are your struggles and challenges living for the sake of Truth?

_____

_____

_____

3. **Resolution for living in Truth & Freedom:** What concrete thing(s) will you do tomorrow to overcome the lies and live more fully in the truth, no matter the cost?

_____

_____

4. **A Daily Record of the Truth:** What thoughts, truths, or observations do you want to record today so that they cannot be erased or forgotten?

_____

_____

_____

_____

_____

_____

Day 332

1. **Gratitude Exercise:** What is one extraordinarily beautiful truth about the world that you noticed today?

_____

_____

_____

2. **Examine Your Actions:** Where have you been challenged today? Where have you compromised the truth or fail to live up to the fullness of justice? What are your struggles and challenges living for the sake of Truth?

_____

_____

_____

3. **Resolution for living in Truth & Freedom:** What concrete thing(s) will you do tomorrow to overcome the lies and live more fully in the truth, no matter the cost?

_____

_____

4. **A Daily Record of the Truth:** What thoughts, truths, or observations do you want to record today so that they cannot be erased or forgotten?

_____

_____

_____

_____

_____

_____

Day 333

1. **Gratitude Exercise:** What is one extraordinarily beautiful truth about the world that you noticed today?

_____

_____

_____

2. **Examine Your Actions:** Where have you been challenged today? Where have you compromised the truth or fail to live up to the fullness of justice? What are your struggles and challenges living for the sake of Truth?

_____

_____

_____

3. **Resolution for living in Truth & Freedom:** What concrete thing(s) will you do tomorrow to overcome the lies and live more fully in the truth, no matter the cost?

_____

_____

4. **A Daily Record of the Truth:** What thoughts, truths, or observations do you want to record today so that they cannot be erased or forgotten?

_____

_____

_____

_____

_____

_____

Day 334

1. **Gratitude Exercise:** What is one extraordinarily beautiful truth about the world that you noticed today?

    _____

    _____

    _____

2. **Examine Your Actions:** Where have you been challenged today? Where have you compromised the truth or fail to live up to the fullness of justice? What are your struggles and challenges living for the sake of Truth?

    _____

    _____

    _____

3. **Resolution for living in Truth & Freedom:** What concrete thing(s) will you do tomorrow to overcome the lies and live more fully in the truth, no matter the cost?

    _____

    _____

4. **A Daily Record of the Truth:** What thoughts, truths, or observations do you want to record today so that they cannot be erased or forgotten?

    _____

    _____

    _____

    _____

    _____

    _____

Day 335

1. **Gratitude Exercise:** What is one extraordinarily beautiful truth about the world that you noticed today?

_____

_____

_____

2. **Examine Your Actions:** Where have you been challenged today? Where have you compromised the truth or fail to live up to the fullness of justice? What are your struggles and challenges living for the sake of Truth?

_____

_____

_____

3. **Resolution for living in Truth & Freedom:** What concrete thing(s) will you do tomorrow to overcome the lies and live more fully in the truth, no matter the cost?

_____

_____

4. **A Daily Record of the Truth:** What thoughts, truths, or observations do you want to record today so that they cannot be erased or forgotten?

_____

_____

_____

_____

_____

_____

Day 336

1. **Gratitude Exercise:** What is one extraordinarily beautiful truth about the world that you noticed today?

_____

_____

_____

2. **Examine Your Actions:** Where have you been challenged today? Where have you compromised the truth or fail to live up to the fullness of justice? What are your struggles and challenges living for the sake of Truth?

_____

_____

_____

3. **Resolution for living in Truth & Freedom:** What concrete thing(s) will you do tomorrow to overcome the lies and live more fully in the truth, no matter the cost?

_____

_____

4. **A Daily Record of the Truth:** What thoughts, truths, or observations do you want to record today so that they cannot be erased or forgotten?

_____

_____

_____

_____

_____

_____

Day 337

1. **Gratitude Exercise:** What is one extraordinarily beautiful truth about the world that you noticed today?

_____

_____

_____

2. **Examine Your Actions:** Where have you been challenged today? Where have you compromised the truth or fail to live up to the fullness of justice? What are your struggles and challenges living for the sake of Truth?

_____

_____

_____

3. **Resolution for living in Truth & Freedom:** What concrete thing(s) will you do tomorrow to overcome the lies and live more fully in the truth, no matter the cost?

_____

_____

4. **A Daily Record of the Truth:** What thoughts, truths, or observations do you want to record today so that they cannot be erased or forgotten?

_____

_____

_____

_____

_____

_____

Day 338

1. **Gratitude Exercise:** What is one extraordinarily beautiful truth about the world that you noticed today?

    _____

    _____

    _____

2. **Examine Your Actions:** Where have you been challenged today? Where have you compromised the truth or fail to live up to the fullness of justice? What are your struggles and challenges living for the sake of Truth?

    _____

    _____

    _____

3. **Resolution for living in Truth & Freedom:** What concrete thing(s) will you do tomorrow to overcome the lies and live more fully in the truth, no matter the cost?

    _____

    _____

4. **A Daily Record of the Truth:** What thoughts, truths, or observations do you want to record today so that they cannot be erased or forgotten?

    _____

    _____

    _____

    _____

    _____

    _____

Day 339

1. **Gratitude Exercise:** What is one extraordinarily beautiful truth about the world that you noticed today?

_____

_____

_____

2. **Examine Your Actions:** Where have you been challenged today? Where have you compromised the truth or fail to live up to the fullness of justice? What are your struggles and challenges living for the sake of Truth?

_____

_____

_____

3. **Resolution for living in Truth & Freedom:** What concrete thing(s) will you do tomorrow to overcome the lies and live more fully in the truth, no matter the cost?

_____

_____

4. **A Daily Record of the Truth:** What thoughts, truths, or observations do you want to record today so that they cannot be erased or forgotten?

_____

_____

_____

_____

_____

_____

Day 340

1. **Gratitude Exercise:** What is one extraordinarily beautiful truth about the world that you noticed today?

_____

_____

_____

2. **Examine Your Actions:** Where have you been challenged today? Where have you compromised the truth or fail to live up to the fullness of justice? What are your struggles and challenges living for the sake of Truth?

_____

_____

_____

3. **Resolution for living in Truth & Freedom:** What concrete thing(s) will you do tomorrow to overcome the lies and live more fully in the truth, no matter the cost?

_____

_____

4. **A Daily Record of the Truth:** What thoughts, truths, or observations do you want to record today so that they cannot be erased or forgotten?

_____

_____

_____

_____

_____

_____

Day 341

1. **Gratitude Exercise:** What is one extraordinarily beautiful truth about the world that you noticed today?

_____

_____

_____

2. **Examine Your Actions:** Where have you been challenged today? Where have you compromised the truth or fail to live up to the fullness of justice? What are your struggles and challenges living for the sake of Truth?

_____

_____

_____

3. **Resolution for living in Truth & Freedom:** What concrete thing(s) will you do tomorrow to overcome the lies and live more fully in the truth, no matter the cost?

_____

_____

4. **A Daily Record of the Truth:** What thoughts, truths, or observations do you want to record today so that they cannot be erased or forgotten?

_____

_____

_____

_____

_____

_____

Day 342

1. **Gratitude Exercise:** What is one extraordinarily beautiful truth about the world that you noticed today?

   _____

   _____

   _____

2. **Examine Your Actions:** Where have you been challenged today? Where have you compromised the truth or fail to live up to the fullness of justice? What are your struggles and challenges living for the sake of Truth?

   _____

   _____

   _____

3. **Resolution for living in Truth & Freedom:** What concrete thing(s) will you do tomorrow to overcome the lies and live more fully in the truth, no matter the cost?

   _____

   _____

4. **A Daily Record of the Truth:** What thoughts, truths, or observations do you want to record today so that they cannot be erased or forgotten?

   _____

   _____

   _____

   _____

   _____

Day 343

1. **Gratitude Exercise:** What is one extraordinarily beautiful truth about the world that you noticed today?

   _____

   _____

   _____

2. **Examine Your Actions:** Where have you been challenged today? Where have you compromised the truth or fail to live up to the fullness of justice? What are your struggles and challenges living for the sake of Truth?

   _____

   _____

   _____

3. **Resolution for living in Truth & Freedom:** What concrete thing(s) will you do tomorrow to overcome the lies and live more fully in the truth, no matter the cost?

   _____

   _____

4. **A Daily Record of the Truth:** What thoughts, truths, or observations do you want to record today so that they cannot be erased or forgotten?

   _____

   _____

   _____

   _____

   _____

Day 344

1. **Gratitude Exercise:** What is one extraordinarily beautiful truth about the world that you noticed today?

2. **Examine Your Actions:** Where have you been challenged today? Where have you compromised the truth or fail to live up to the fullness of justice? What are your struggles and challenges living for the sake of Truth?

3. **Resolution for living in Truth & Freedom:** What concrete thing(s) will you do tomorrow to overcome the lies and live more fully in the truth, no matter the cost?

4. **A Daily Record of the Truth:** What thoughts, truths, or observations do you want to record today so that they cannot be erased or forgotten?

Day 345

1. **Gratitude Exercise:** What is one extraordinarily beautiful truth about the world that you noticed today?

_____

_____

_____

2. **Examine Your Actions:** Where have you been challenged today? Where have you compromised the truth or fail to live up to the fullness of justice? What are your struggles and challenges living for the sake of Truth?

_____

_____

_____

3. **Resolution for living in Truth & Freedom:** What concrete thing(s) will you do tomorrow to overcome the lies and live more fully in the truth, no matter the cost?

_____

_____

4. **A Daily Record of the Truth:** What thoughts, truths, or observations do you want to record today so that they cannot be erased or forgotten?

_____

_____

_____

_____

_____

_____

Day 346

1. **Gratitude Exercise:** What is one extraordinarily beautiful truth about the world that you noticed today?

   _____

   _____

   _____

2. **Examine Your Actions:** Where have you been challenged today? Where have you compromised the truth or fail to live up to the fullness of justice? What are your struggles and challenges living for the sake of Truth?

   _____

   _____

   _____

3. **Resolution for living in Truth & Freedom:** What concrete thing(s) will you do tomorrow to overcome the lies and live more fully in the truth, no matter the cost?

   _____

   _____

4. **A Daily Record of the Truth:** What thoughts, truths, or observations do you want to record today so that they cannot be erased or forgotten?

   _____

   _____

   _____

   _____

   _____

Day 347

1. **Gratitude Exercise:** What is one extraordinarily beautiful truth about the world that you noticed today?

_____

_____

_____

2. **Examine Your Actions:** Where have you been challenged today? Where have you compromised the truth or fail to live up to the fullness of justice? What are your struggles and challenges living for the sake of Truth?

_____

_____

_____

3. **Resolution for living in Truth & Freedom:** What concrete thing(s) will you do tomorrow to overcome the lies and live more fully in the truth, no matter the cost?

_____

_____

4. **A Daily Record of the Truth:** What thoughts, truths, or observations do you want to record today so that they cannot be erased or forgotten?

_____

_____

_____

_____

_____

Day 348

1. **Gratitude Exercise:** What is one extraordinarily beautiful truth about the world that you noticed today?

_____

_____

_____

2. **Examine Your Actions:** Where have you been challenged today? Where have you compromised the truth or fail to live up to the fullness of justice? What are your struggles and challenges living for the sake of Truth?

_____

_____

_____

3. **Resolution for living in Truth & Freedom:** What concrete thing(s) will you do tomorrow to overcome the lies and live more fully in the truth, no matter the cost?

_____

_____

4. **A Daily Record of the Truth:** What thoughts, truths, or observations do you want to record today so that they cannot be erased or forgotten?

_____

_____

_____

_____

_____

Day 349

1. **Gratitude Exercise:** What is one extraordinarily beautiful truth about the world that you noticed today?

_____

_____

_____

2. **Examine Your Actions:** Where have you been challenged today? Where have you compromised the truth or fail to live up to the fullness of justice? What are your struggles and challenges living for the sake of Truth?

_____

_____

_____

3. **Resolution for living in Truth & Freedom:** What concrete thing(s) will you do tomorrow to overcome the lies and live more fully in the truth, no matter the cost?

_____

_____

4. **A Daily Record of the Truth:** What thoughts, truths, or observations do you want to record today so that they cannot be erased or forgotten?

_____

_____

_____

_____

_____

Day 350

1. **Gratitude Exercise:** What is one extraordinarily beautiful truth about the world that you noticed today?

_____

_____

_____

2. **Examine Your Actions:** Where have you been challenged today? Where have you compromised the truth or fail to live up to the fullness of justice? What are your struggles and challenges living for the sake of Truth?

_____

_____

_____

3. **Resolution for living in Truth & Freedom:** What concrete thing(s) will you do tomorrow to overcome the lies and live more fully in the truth, no matter the cost?

_____

_____

4. **A Daily Record of the Truth:** What thoughts, truths, or observations do you want to record today so that they cannot be erased or forgotten?

_____

_____

_____

_____

_____

_____

Day 351

1. **Gratitude Exercise:** What is one extraordinarily beautiful truth about the world that you noticed today?

_____

_____

_____

2. **Examine Your Actions:** Where have you been challenged today? Where have you compromised the truth or fail to live up to the fullness of justice? What are your struggles and challenges living for the sake of Truth?

_____

_____

_____

3. **Resolution for living in Truth & Freedom:** What concrete thing(s) will you do tomorrow to overcome the lies and live more fully in the truth, no matter the cost?

_____

_____

4. **A Daily Record of the Truth:** What thoughts, truths, or observations do you want to record today so that they cannot be erased or forgotten?

_____

_____

_____

_____

_____

Day 352

1. **Gratitude Exercise:** What is one extraordinarily beautiful truth about the world that you noticed today?

_____

_____

_____

2. **Examine Your Actions:** Where have you been challenged today? Where have you compromised the truth or fail to live up to the fullness of justice? What are your struggles and challenges living for the sake of Truth?

_____

_____

_____

3. **Resolution for living in Truth & Freedom:** What concrete thing(s) will you do tomorrow to overcome the lies and live more fully in the truth, no matter the cost?

_____

_____

4. **A Daily Record of the Truth:** What thoughts, truths, or observations do you want to record today so that they cannot be erased or forgotten?

_____

_____

_____

_____

_____

_____

Day 353

1. **Gratitude Exercise:** What is one extraordinarily beautiful truth about the world that you noticed today?

---

2. **Examine Your Actions:** Where have you been challenged today? Where have you compromised the truth or fail to live up to the fullness of justice? What are your struggles and challenges living for the sake of Truth?

---

3. **Resolution for living in Truth & Freedom:** What concrete thing(s) will you do tomorrow to overcome the lies and live more fully in the truth, no matter the cost?

---

4. **A Daily Record of the Truth:** What thoughts, truths, or observations do you want to record today so that they cannot be erased or forgotten?

Day 354

1. **Gratitude Exercise:** What is one extraordinarily beautiful truth about the world that you noticed today?

_____

_____

_____

2. **Examine Your Actions:** Where have you been challenged today? Where have you compromised the truth or fail to live up to the fullness of justice? What are your struggles and challenges living for the sake of Truth?

_____

_____

_____

3. **Resolution for living in Truth & Freedom:** What concrete thing(s) will you do tomorrow to overcome the lies and live more fully in the truth, no matter the cost?

_____

_____

4. **A Daily Record of the Truth:** What thoughts, truths, or observations do you want to record today so that they cannot be erased or forgotten?

_____

_____

_____

_____

_____

_____

Day 355

1. **Gratitude Exercise:** What is one extraordinarily beautiful truth about the world that you noticed today?

    _____

    _____

    _____

2. **Examine Your Actions:** Where have you been challenged today? Where have you compromised the truth or fail to live up to the fullness of justice? What are your struggles and challenges living for the sake of Truth?

    _____

    _____

    _____

3. **Resolution for living in Truth & Freedom:** What concrete thing(s) will you do tomorrow to overcome the lies and live more fully in the truth, no matter the cost?

    _____

    _____

4. **A Daily Record of the Truth:** What thoughts, truths, or observations do you want to record today so that they cannot be erased or forgotten?

    _____

    _____

    _____

    _____

    _____

    _____

Day 356

1. **Gratitude Exercise:** What is one extraordinarily beautiful truth about the world that you noticed today?

_____

_____

_____

2. **Examine Your Actions:** Where have you been challenged today? Where have you compromised the truth or fail to live up to the fullness of justice? What are your struggles and challenges living for the sake of Truth?

_____

_____

_____

3. **Resolution for living in Truth & Freedom:** What concrete thing(s) will you do tomorrow to overcome the lies and live more fully in the truth, no matter the cost?

_____

_____

4. **A Daily Record of the Truth:** What thoughts, truths, or observations do you want to record today so that they cannot be erased or forgotten?

_____

_____

_____

_____

_____

_____

Day 357

1. **Gratitude Exercise:** What is one extraordinarily beautiful truth about the world that you noticed today?

_____

_____

_____

2. **Examine Your Actions:** Where have you been challenged today? Where have you compromised the truth or fail to live up to the fullness of justice? What are your struggles and challenges living for the sake of Truth?

_____

_____

_____

3. **Resolution for living in Truth & Freedom:** What concrete thing(s) will you do tomorrow to overcome the lies and live more fully in the truth, no matter the cost?

_____

_____

4. **A Daily Record of the Truth:** What thoughts, truths, or observations do you want to record today so that they cannot be erased or forgotten?

_____

_____

_____

_____

_____

_____

Day 358

1. **Gratitude Exercise:** What is one extraordinarily beautiful truth about the world that you noticed today?

_____

_____

_____

2. **Examine Your Actions:** Where have you been challenged today? Where have you compromised the truth or fail to live up to the fullness of justice? What are your struggles and challenges living for the sake of Truth?

_____

_____

_____

3. **Resolution for living in Truth & Freedom:** What concrete thing(s) will you do tomorrow to overcome the lies and live more fully in the truth, no matter the cost?

_____

_____

4. **A Daily Record of the Truth:** What thoughts, truths, or observations do you want to record today so that they cannot be erased or forgotten?

_____

_____

_____

_____

_____

Day 359

1. **Gratitude Exercise:** What is one extraordinarily beautiful truth about the world that you noticed today?

_____

_____

_____

2. **Examine Your Actions:** Where have you been challenged today? Where have you compromised the truth or fail to live up to the fullness of justice? What are your struggles and challenges living for the sake of Truth?

_____

_____

_____

3. **Resolution for living in Truth & Freedom:** What concrete thing(s) will you do tomorrow to overcome the lies and live more fully in the truth, no matter the cost?

_____

_____

4. **A Daily Record of the Truth:** What thoughts, truths, or observations do you want to record today so that they cannot be erased or forgotten?

_____

_____

_____

_____

_____

Day 360

1. **Gratitude Exercise:** What is one extraordinarily beautiful truth about the world that you noticed today?

_____

_____

_____

2. **Examine Your Actions:** Where have you been challenged today? Where have you compromised the truth or fail to live up to the fullness of justice? What are your struggles and challenges living for the sake of Truth?

_____

_____

_____

3. **Resolution for living in Truth & Freedom:** What concrete thing(s) will you do tomorrow to overcome the lies and live more fully in the truth, no matter the cost?

_____

_____

4. **A Daily Record of the Truth:** What thoughts, truths, or observations do you want to record today so that they cannot be erased or forgotten?

_____

_____

_____

_____

_____

Day 361

1. **Gratitude Exercise:** What is one extraordinarily beautiful truth about the world that you noticed today?

_____

_____

_____

2. **Examine Your Actions:** Where have you been challenged today? Where have you compromised the truth or fail to live up to the fullness of justice? What are your struggles and challenges living for the sake of Truth?

_____

_____

_____

3. **Resolution for living in Truth & Freedom:** What concrete thing(s) will you do tomorrow to overcome the lies and live more fully in the truth, no matter the cost?

_____

_____

4. **A Daily Record of the Truth:** What thoughts, truths, or observations do you want to record today so that they cannot be erased or forgotten?

_____

_____

_____

_____

_____

Day 362

1. **Gratitude Exercise:** What is one extraordinarily beautiful truth about the world that you noticed today?

_____

_____

_____

2. **Examine Your Actions:** Where have you been challenged today? Where have you compromised the truth or fail to live up to the fullness of justice? What are your struggles and challenges living for the sake of Truth?

_____

_____

_____

3. **Resolution for living in Truth & Freedom:** What concrete thing(s) will you do tomorrow to overcome the lies and live more fully in the truth, no matter the cost?

_____

_____

4. **A Daily Record of the Truth:** What thoughts, truths, or observations do you want to record today so that they cannot be erased or forgotten?

_____

_____

_____

_____

_____

Day 363

1. **Gratitude Exercise:** What is one extraordinarily beautiful truth about the world that you noticed today?

_____

_____

_____

2. **Examine Your Actions:** Where have you been challenged today? Where have you compromised the truth or fail to live up to the fullness of justice? What are your struggles and challenges living for the sake of Truth?

_____

_____

_____

3. **Resolution for living in Truth & Freedom:** What concrete thing(s) will you do tomorrow to overcome the lies and live more fully in the truth, no matter the cost?

_____

_____

4. **A Daily Record of the Truth:** What thoughts, truths, or observations do you want to record today so that they cannot be erased or forgotten?

_____

_____

_____

_____

_____

Day 364

1. **Gratitude Exercise:** What is one extraordinarily beautiful truth about the world that you noticed today?

_____

_____

_____

2. **Examine Your Actions:** Where have you been challenged today? Where have you compromised the truth or fail to live up to the fullness of justice? What are your struggles and challenges living for the sake of Truth?

_____

_____

_____

3. **Resolution for living in Truth & Freedom:** What concrete thing(s) will you do tomorrow to overcome the lies and live more fully in the truth, no matter the cost?

_____

_____

4. **A Daily Record of the Truth:** What thoughts, truths, or observations do you want to record today so that they cannot be erased or forgotten?

_____

_____

_____

_____

_____

Day 365

1. **Gratitude Exercise:** What is one extraordinarily beautiful truth about the world that you noticed today?

_____

_____

_____

2. **Examine Your Actions:** Where have you been challenged today? Where have you compromised the truth or fail to live up to the fullness of justice? What are your struggles and challenges living for the sake of Truth?

_____

_____

_____

3. **Resolution for living in Truth & Freedom:** What concrete thing(s) will you do tomorrow to overcome the lies and live more fully in the truth, no matter the cost?

_____

_____

4. **A Daily Record of the Truth:** What thoughts, truths, or observations do you want to record today so that they cannot be erased or forgotten?

_____

_____

_____

_____

_____

ONLY THE BEGINNING

Congratulations on completing one whole year of interior freedom in pursuit of, and living in, the truth. You have created a beautiful work in here, and a powerful witness both to yourself and to anyone whom you choose to share it with. I hope you will continue on this journey to seek the truth and commit to live not by lies.

Manufactured by Amazon.ca
Bolton, ON

20958732R00210